Experimental Neuropsychology

A SERIES OF BOOKS IN PSYCHOLOGY

Editor: Stanley Coopersmith

Experimental Neuropsychology

A LABORATORY MANUAL

Benjamin L. Hart

UNIVERSITY OF CALIFORNIA, DAVIS

W. H. FREEMAN AND COMPANY
SAN FRANCISCO

Preface

Neuropsychology is that science concerned with the function of the central nervous system in behavior. It is one of the most important aspects of physiological psychology. The laboratory experiments in neuropsychology are intriguing, but student participation in them is too often limited because of the complex procedures and expensive equipment usually employed. This is unfortunate because many of the significant advances in this field are most meaningful if one has direct familiarity with the laboratory or experimental aspects. This manual is designed to introduce you, by sequential steps, to experimental neuropsychology. Because inexpensive equipment, rather than the expensive apparatus used in research, is designated, it allows you to participate in experiments in which you will alter brain function by stereotaxic brain surgery and then test the behavioral effects of the alteration.

This manual is intended for upper division or beginning graduate courses in neuropsychology, and it is assumed that you will have had at least one college course in both psychology and biology. Your maximum participation in all aspects of the laboratory work is expected.

It is imperative, of course, that you know something about the structure of the central nervous system if you are to understand its function in behavior. For this reason, the purpose of the first section of this manual is to acquaint you with the gross and subgross structure of the mammalian brain. Study of three species—rat, ruminant, human—will give you a rough idea of comparative differences and similarities in the brains of mammals. The rat is included in this section because it is the animal that you will be using in neuropsychological experiments of the third section. The ruminant is important because cow and sheep brains, besides being readily available for dissection, are large enough that most of the important structures can be seen with the naked eye. Because much of the work in neuropsychology is done with the hope of eventually extending the results to the human species, the human brain, too, is included for general examination. Also, you are probably most interested in the brain of your own species. The first section also introduces a method of sectioning, staining, and examining the internal structure of the rat brain.

In the second section of the manual you will become familiar with the procedures of stereotaxic brain surgery on the rat. Procedures for making electrodes, anesthetizing rats, using stereotaxic coordinates, and performing surgery on the head are outlined.

The third section consists of a group of neuropsychological experiments which utilize the information and techniques learned in the previous sections. In addition to studying some specific behavioral changes that follow alteration of the brain, you will learn about some of the conceptual problems, as well as about the advantages and disadvantages of various experimental approaches to neuropsychology. The laboratory rat is used in these experiments because these animals have been studied extensively in psychological research. Also, they are less expensive and easier to maintain than other animals. The experiments are intended only as examples. Because of the rapid progress in neuropsychology, and the diverse interests that exist among different instructors, your instructor may want to pursue experiments other than those in this manual, or in addition to them.

The fourth section of this manual is an atlas of the rat brain. This will be of aid in learning about the structure of the brain as well as in doing the neuropsychological experiments.

The manual is so designed that it should take about ten 3- or 4-hour laboratory periods for a team of students (2 to 4) to accomplish the exercises and experiments presented. Three periods should be allotted to study of brain structure as it is outlined in Parts A, B, and C of Section 1; one period should be devoted to each part. It is suggested that two periods be spent practicing stereotaxic surgery, but on dead animals, as outlined in Section 2: one period should be devoted to lesion procedures, and one to electrode implantation procedures. Five periods should be devoted to the neuropsychological experiments in Section 3. Like most work in neuropsychology, these experiments will require more than one laboratory period for completion. But since the amount of work that can be done on any particular experiment will not take a full period, several experiments can be conducted simultaneously. Your instructor will probably provide you with a program of procedures to be completed each period.

At the end of each of the first three sections there is a short list of references to provide you with sources of additional information. Also listed are commercial sources of equipment and supplies other than standard laboratory materials and equipment that will be needed for study of a particular section.

January, 1969

BENJAMIN L. HART

Contents

THE STRUCTURE OF THE MAMMALIAN CENTRAL NERVOUS SYSTEM

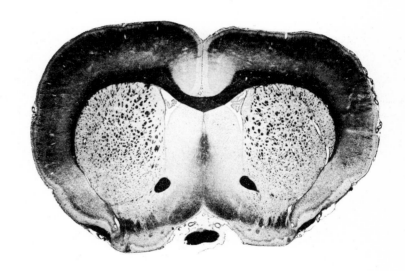

INTRODUCTION

An understanding of the function of the central nervous system requires some knowledge of basic sturcture of the brain and spinal cord. In the first part of this section you will be examining the surface features of the spinal cord, whole brain, and brain stem of the ruminant and human species. In the second part you will dissect the ruminant brain to obtain a three-dimensional perspective of the cerebral hemispheres and brain stem of the mammalian brain. In the third part you will dissect the rat brain and examine surface features under the stereomicroscope.

Because many important structures cannot be seen on the surface, you will need to study the internal structure of the brain as represented in thin sections. A list of the necessary materials is given at the end of the section.

Since this section deals mostly with examination and dissection of the central nervous system, you will find your laboratory work most meaningful if you read about the gross anatomy of the brain and spinal cord in a basic neuroanatomy text before beginning laboratory work.

Surface Features of the Ruminant Brain, the Human Brain, and the Spinal Cord

NEURONS

Before gross examination of the brain and spinal cord is begun, something should be said about the elements they comprise. The central nervous system is composed of neurons and supporting cells referred to as neuroglia. In the human brain there are about 10 billion neurons, and about 10 times as many glial cells, which play an important role in maintaining nutrition and metabolism for neurons. Most neurons in the central nervous system have dendritic ramifications and an axon extending from the cell body. The dendritic ramifications, which convey the electrochemical neural influences from presynaptic elements toward the cell body, are rather short and the axon, which conducts nerve impulses away from the cell body, can be quite long. The various parts of a typical multipolar neuron are labeled in Figure 1-1.

When cell bodies are collected together within a discrete group these areas are referred to as nuclei. Thus, the term nucleus referring to a group of neurons should be differentiated from the nucleus of a single cell.

THE SPINAL CORD AND SPINAL MENINGES

Place the section of spinal cord provided for dissection in a pan, after rinsing off excess formalin with tap water. The cord will probably be covered with protective membranes. These are the three layers of spinal meninges of which the dura mater is the outermost. Slit the dura with scissors and carefully pull it

back to see if you can see the web-like middle layer of the meninges, the arachnoid. In the live animal the arachnoid is closely applied to the dura; beneath the arachnoid is the subarachnoid space. The innermost layer of the meninges, the pia mater, is closely applied to the spinal cord and is not readily seen. If the spinal roots are intact, observe their emergence from the sides of the cord. On each side there is a dorsal (posterior) root conveying nerve impulses for sensory information toward the spinal cord, and a ventral (anterior) root conveying nerve impulses for motor function away from the spinal cord. These roots join distal to the cord to form a spinal nerve. Just prox-

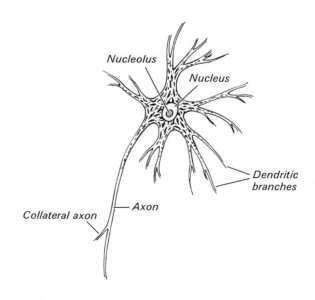

FIGURE 1-1. *Typical multipolar neuron.*

4

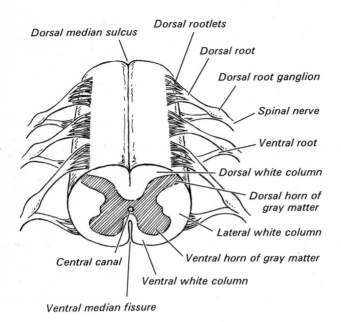

FIGURE 1-2. *Schematic view of the spinal cord (cervical section).*

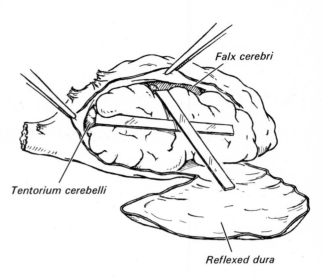

FIGURE 1-3. *The falx cerebri and tentorium cerebelli of the bovine brain.*

imal to the union of the roots (forming a spinal nerve) you may find an enlargement of the dorsal root. This enlargement, the spinal or dorsal root ganglion, consists mostly of cell bodies of neurons, the axons of which are traveling in the dorsal root. On the sides of the spinal cord, between the areas of which spinal roots emerge from the cord, try to find the dentate ligaments that extend from the pia on the lateral aspects of the cord to the dura. These aid in suspending the cord within the subarachnoid space.

Next, carefully dissect the dura and arachnoid from two or three segments of the spinal cord in order to examine the main features of the cord more fully. The spinal cords of all mammals are very similar and the typical arrangement of the spinal cord is shown in Figure 1-2. Note the oval shape of a transverse section. If your section is from the cervical region you may see a portion of the spinal accessory nerve (carnial nerve) running along both sides of the cord. Locate the dorsal (posterior) median sulcus and the ventral (anterior) median fissure. A vertical line drawn through these two fissures divides the cord into symmetrical halves. Note where the spinal roots enter the cord. Two longitudinal lines drawn on each side down the length of the cord and passing thorugh the points at which roots enter or leave the cord divide each half of the cord into a dorsal portion (dorsal column), a lateral portion (lateral column), and a ventral portion (ventral column).

With a scalpel cut a thin slice of spinal cord and examine it under the stereomicroscope (which should be illuminated from above). Locate the dorsal and ventral horns of the gray matter (nerve cell bodies) and the dorsal, lateral and ventral white columns (nerve fibers). The dorsal gray region contains neurons mediating mostly sensory function and the ventral gray region contains neurons mediating mostly motor or effector function. The dorsal, lateral and ventral white columns contain nerve fibers that transfer nerve impulses either up or down the spinal cord.

CRANIAL MENINGES

Rinse off with water the ruminant brain that has been provided for your dissection. The brain may be completely surrounded by the protective meninges and in some places bone may remain adhered to the dura. In the cranial cavity there are two layers of dura and the layer you see is the outer layer of cranial dura. If the brain you have is covered by dura, cut away the dura overlying the cerebral hemispheres and examine the falx cerebri extending between the cerebral hemispheres (Figures 1-3). This membrane is formed by the inward reflection of the inner layer of cranial dura. One of the major venous sinuses of the brain, the dorsal sagittal sinus, is located at the site at which the falx meets the outer layer of cranial dura. Cut the dura overlying the cerebellar area and examine the tentorium cerebelli (Figure 1-3). This membrane is also formed by an inward reflection of inner dura. Next slit (with scissors) the dura on the posterior as-

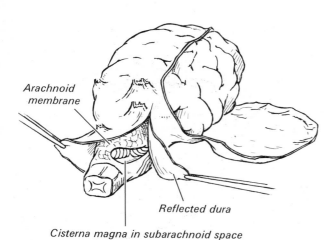

Arachnoid
membrane

Reflected dura

Cisterna magna in subarachnoid space

FIGURE 1-4. *Exposure of the cisterna magna.*

pect of the brain. Pull the flaps of dura aside and identify the cisterna magna, which is part of the subarachnoid space (Figure 1-4). This is the largest subarachnoid cavity (cistern) of cerebrospinal fluid, which fills the ventricles and subarachnoid spaces. Taps for cerebrospinal fluid from domestic animals are frequently taken from this space.

Slit the dura on the ventral surface of the brain up to the level of the junction of the optic nerves (optic chiasm), encircle the optic nerves with a cut, and continue the incision anteriorly. Carefully peel the dura from the brain and examine the emergence of cranial nerves from the brain while you are doing this. Identify the optic (II), oculomotor (III), trigeminal (V), facial (VII), and statoacoustic (VIII) cranial nerves (Figure 1-6,*b*). The trigeminal (Gasserian) and facial (Geniculate) ganglia, for the trigeminal and facial nerves respectively, are buried in the dura (and possibly in the bone on your specimen) and are quite difficult to dissect. The remaining cranial nerves—trochlear (IV), abducens (VI), glossopharyngeal (IX), vagus (X), spinal accessory (XI), and hypoglossal (XII)—are small, or they emerge from the brain as rootlets. Because these nerves are difficult to distinguish in most specimens and are easily ripped from the brain, you should not spend much time looking for them.

You may find a great deal of coagulated blood (dark brown) inside the dura on the ventral side of the brain. This is due to a rupture of cerebral arteries as a result of the penetration of a captive bolt which

was used to kill the animal humanely. You will have to remove the blood clots carefully with thumb forceps to expose some cranial nerves and certain structures on the ventral part of the brain.

SURFACE FEATURES OF THE BRAIN

After cleaning off meninges an blood vessels, you will examine the surface features of the brain. Frequent reference to the outline below and to Figures 1-5 and 1-6 help you.

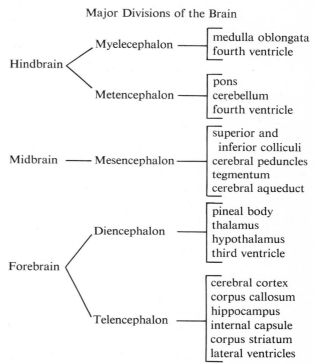

Major Divisions of the Brain

Hindbrain
- Myelecephalon — medulla oblongata / fourth ventricle
- Metencephalon — pons / cerebellum / fourth ventricle

Midbrain — Mesencephalon — superior and inferior colliculi / cerebral peduncles / tegmentum / cerebral aqueduct

Forebrain
- Diencephalon — pineal body / thalamus / hypothalamus / third ventricle
- Telencephalon — cerebral cortex / corpus callosum / hippocampus / internal capsule / corpus striatum / lateral ventricles

Brain stem — This consists of the hindbrain, except for the cerebellum, the midbrain, and the forebrain, except for the cerebral hemispheres.

Cerebral Hemispheres — These consist of the cerebral cortex and underlying white matter, the corpus callosum, and the hippocampus.

On the dorsal aspect of the ruminant and human brains observe the cerebral hemispheres and cerebellum. The cerebral hemispheres are separated by a longitudinal fissure. The two hemispheres together make up the cerebrum. The cerebellum appears relatively larger in the subprimate brain because the cerebrum is smaller and does not obscure the cerebellum as much.

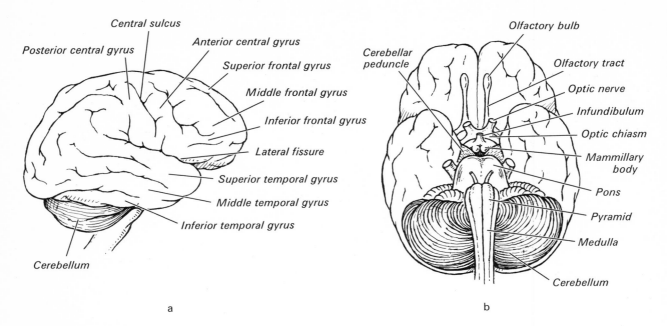

FIGURE 1-5. *The human brain:* a. *lateral aspect;* b. *ventral aspect;* c. *ventral aspect, with cerebellum and pons removed;* d. *midsagittal view;* e. *dorsal aspect of the brain stem.*

On the ventral aspect of each brain locate the medulla (medulla oblongata), pons, mammillary bodies (in the human brain these are paired and hence breast-like), optic nerves, and optic chiasm. Behind the optic chiasm, you should be able to locate an elevated prominence with a hole in it. This is the stem or infundibulum of the pituitary gland. The pituitary gland has been separated from the forebrain of most brains when they have been removed from the skull. The hole you see is a recess of the third ventricle into the infundibulum. Trace the ventral median fissure, which is a forward continuation of the same fissure in the spinal cord. The ridges running parallel to the ventral median fissure (in the region of the medulla) are the pyramids.

GYRI AND SULCI
OF THE CEREBRAL CORTEX

Examine the cerebral hemispheres and note the highly convoluted system of folds or gyri of the cerebral cortex. The gyri are separated by crevices or fissures called sulci. All of the various gyri and sulci of different species have names, but for our purposes it is sufficient to recognize only a few of the larger sulci and important gyri. Since the basic terminology is derived from the anatomy of the human cerebrum, it is suggested that you examine the human brain before the ruminant brain. On the human brain find the cen-

tral sulcus, which is located about midway between the anterior and posterior poles of the cerebrum. It is not always easy to identify this sulcus; in most brains, it is the longest of the sulci. The gyrus just in front of this sulcus, the precentral gyrus, is the main motor cortex. The gyrus just behind the central sulcus, the postcentral gyrus, is the chief sensory projection area for cutaneous sensation. A large fissure easily distinguished on the lateral aspect is the lateral cerebral fissure (of Sylvius).

The central sulcus and lateral fissure can be used to divide the cerebral cortex roughly into different regions. The frontal lobe is the region in front of the central sulcus and above the lateral cerebral fissure. The temporal lobe is the region lying below the lateral cerebral fissure. The occipital lobe is a smaller region located around the posterior or occipital pole of the hemisphere. The parietal lobe lies between the frontal and occipital lobes. It will not be easy for you to outline the exact boundaries of the parietal and occipital lobes.

On the ruminant brain identify the transverse sulcus, which is somewhat analogous to the central sulcus of the human brain, since it separates the motor cortex (anterior) from the sensory cortex (posterior). Find the lateral fissure and roughly outline the frontal, temporal, parietal, and occipital lobes of the ruminant brain. Locate the rhinal fissure and the pyriform lobe just below. The pyriform area is not visible on the human brain because it is covered by

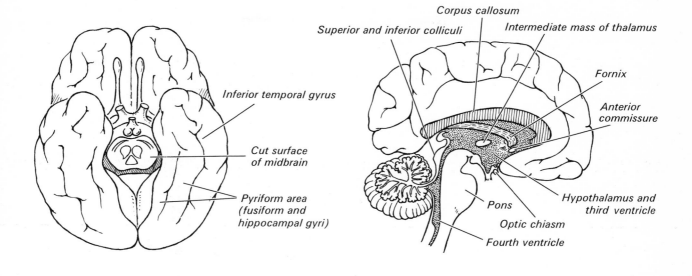

Inferior temporal gyrus

Cut surface of midbrain

Pyriform area (fusiform and hippocampal gyri)

c

Corpus callosum

Superior and inferior colliculi

Intermediate mass of thalamus

Fornix

Anterior commissure

Hypothalamus and third ventricle

Pons

Optic chiasm

Fourth ventricle

d

the expanded temporal lobe and cerebellum. In Figure 1-5c you can get some idea of that region of the human brain homologous to the pyriform lobe of ruminants, but that cannot be completely seen in the undissected human brain.

Next, examine the ruminant brain stem.* The term "brain stem" is used to describe the brain from which the cerebellum and cerebral hemispheres have been removed.

Before we continue, a word should be said about the ventricular system of the brain. Within the brain there are four cavities that contain cerebrospinal fluid. These cavities are the lateral ventricles (first and second), and the third and fourth ventricles. Fluid is formed in each cavity and flows from the lateral ventricles to the third through the intraventricular foramena, and from the third to the fourth through the cerebral aqueduct (of Sylvius). From the fourth ventricle fluid escapes into the cisterna magna of the subarachnoid space through small openings. Examine the rhomboid fossa, which forms the floor of the fourth ventricle. The cerebellum, with its attached anterior and posterior membranes, normally lies on top of the rhomboid fossa and forms the roof of the fourth ventricle. In the whole brain the cerebellum is attached to the brain stem on each side by

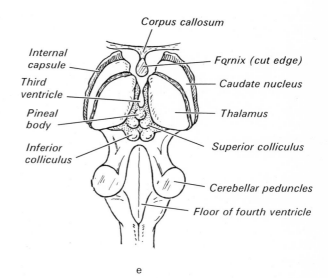

Corpus callosum

Internal capsule

Third ventricle

Pineal body

Inferior colliculus

Fornix (cut edge)

Caudate nucleus

Thalamus

Superior colliculus

Cerebellar peduncles

Floor of fourth ventricle

e

three cerebellar peduncles (bundles of nerve fibers). These peduncles are located very close together but the largest can easily be identified. This is the middle peduncle or brachium pontis (arm of the pons). Trace the fibers running transversely from the pons up into the brachium pontis and to the site at which the fibers have been severed for removal of the cerebellum. The most anterior peduncle is the brachium conjunctivum, and the most posterior peduncle is the restiform body.

Locate the cerebral aqueduct extending forward from the fourth ventricle to the third ventricle. The cerebral aqueduct transverses the region of the midbrain (mesencephalon). On top of the midbrain (dorsal to the aqueduct and anterior to the floor of the

*Suggestion to instructor: Brain stems resulting from dissection (Part B) of previous classes may be used. Initial supply of brain stems should be dissected from whole brains.

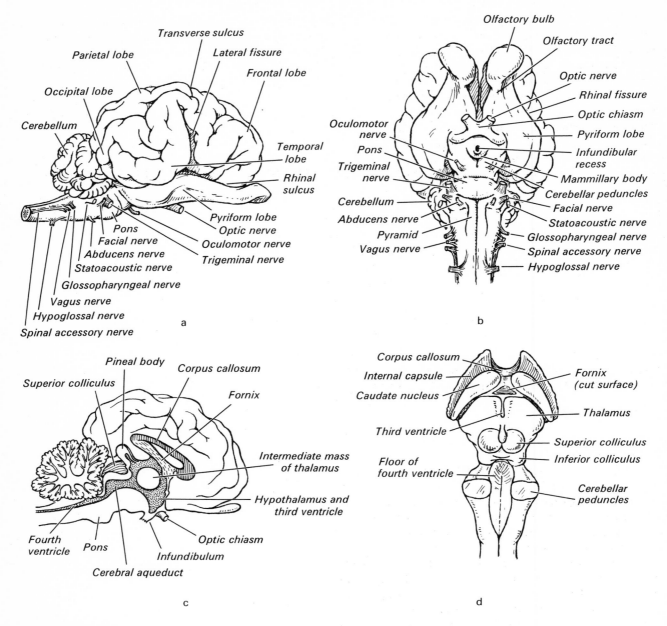

FIGURE 1-6. *The ruminant brain: a. lateral aspect; b. ventral aspect; c. midsagittal view; d. dorsal aspect of the brain stem.*

fourth ventricle) are four rounded bodies, the paired inferior colliculi and the paired superior colliculi. The colliculi, which are much smaller in the human brain than in the other brains, are nuclei of gray matter that are primarily reflex centers for the auditory (inferior colliculi) and visual (superior colliculi) systems. These four structures together are called the corpora quadrigemina.

On the ventral surface of the midbrain, just ahead of the pons, find two longitudinally directed large fiber bundles. These are the cerebral peduncles. These peduncles consist partially of nerve fibers extending from the cerebral cortex to the pons, medulla, and spinal cord. The pyramids, in the medulla, are the posterior continuations of nerve fibers in the cerebral peduncles.

Locate the massive thalamus anterior to the superior colliculi. The thalamus, which is actually a paired structure, is a complex of several nuclei of nerve cells. These thalamic nuclei are important synaptic or relay centers for almost all sensory systems. Much of the space of the third ventricle is located between the halves of the thalamus. Find the angular groove anterior and lateral to the side of the thalamus. This groove forms a boundary between the thalamus and another large nucleus of nerve cells, the caudate nucleus. The caudate nucleus is part of a complex of nuclei referred to as the corpus striatum and is functionally related to control of skeletal movements. Anterior and lateral to the caudate nucleus, find the cut edge of the internal capsule. This large fan-shaped bundle of nerve fibers consists of fibers passing between the thalamus and cerebral cortex, as well as of others that pass from the cerebral cortex to the pons, medulla, and spinal cord, by means of the cerebral peduncles, for motor control. You should be able to follow some of the fibers that are part of the internal capsule through the cerebral peduncles.

Locate again on the ventral surface the optic nerves and the optic chiasm. Follow the continuation of optic nerve fibers, as the optic tract, across the surface of the cerebral peduncles and into the thalamic region.

Dissection of the Ruminant Brain

In this exercise you will use a brain (of a cow or a sheep) that has been specially prepared for dissection by freezing and rethawing.* This technique makes it easier to separate gray matter (nerve cells) from white matter (nerve fibers). You will first remove the cerebellum and then dissect away the cerebral hemispheres bit by bit, identifying important structures as you proceed. You will finally end up with the brain stem, similar to that which was studied in Part A.

REMOVAL AND EXAMINATION OF THE CEREBELLUM

Remove any remaining meninges and blood vessels from the brain. Trace the brachium pontis into the cerebellum. Pull one side of the cerebellum away from the brain stem and, with a scalpel, carefully cut through the cerebellar peduncles (Figure 1-7a). You will be most successful in this operation if you angle the scalpel blade toward the midline and down (ventromedially). Sever the cerebellar peduncles on both sides and pull off the cerebellum. Note the extent of the fourth ventricle as you remove the cerebellum. Make a midsagittal cut through the cerebellum, dividing it into symmetrical halves (Figure 1-7,b). On the cut surface note the tree-shaped medullary core of nerve fibers. The medullary core branches into rays that are covered by a thin layer of cerebellar cortex (gray matter).

_____

*Suggestion to instructor: Brains should have been frozen in air-tight plastic bags in deep freeze for 3 to 4 days and subsequently rethawed in formalin solution.

REMOVAL OF CORTICAL SUBSTANCE

Review the major gyri and sulci of the ruminant brain that were identified in Part A, and find these on the brain you are using. In the center of each gyrus of the brain there is a core or projection of nerve fibers. Expose this medullary core by opening each sulcus and peeling the cortex from each major gyrus with a pair of forceps, a broken orange stick, or the blunt end of a scalpel. Remove the cortex from both hemispheres down to the rhinal sulcus, leaving the pyriform lobe intact. Cut off the medullary core with scissors so that only about $\frac{1}{4}$ inch sticks up. It may help to cut off the medullary cores before all of the cortex has been peeled out. Your dissection at this point should look something like Figure 1-7,c.

The white matter that has been exposed consists of three types of nerve fibers:

1) Association fibers, which connect one area of the cerebral cortex with other areas of the same hemisphere. There are both long association fibers, running from one lobe to another, and short association fibers, running from one gyrus to an adjacent gyrus.

2) Commissural fibers, which connect analogous areas of each cerebral hemisphere with the other side through the corpus callosum.

3) Internal capsule—composed of fibers passing between the thalamus and various areas of the cerebral cortex as well as fibers passing from motor cells in the cortex to structures in the brain stem and spinal cord.

Using forceps, tear away the plates of medullary

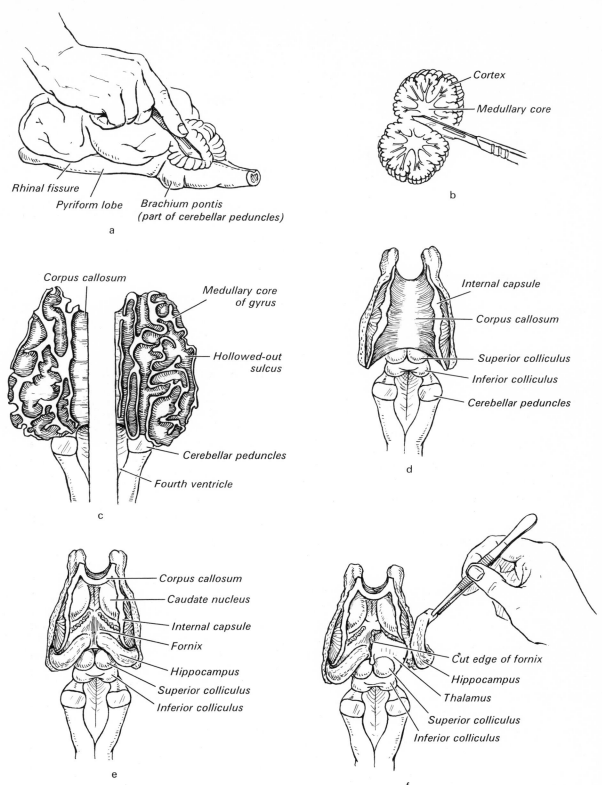

FIGURE 1-7. a. *Cutting the brachium pontis in preparation for removal of the cerebellum;* b. *Midsagittal view of the cerebellum.* c. *Appearance of the brain with the cerebellum removed and with the cortical substance removed from the gyri; on the left side, some of the medullary cores of smaller gyri have been removed.* d. *Appearance of the brain with the medullary cores removed; a thin shell of corpus callosum remains.* e. *Appearance of the brain with the internal capsule fully exposed and the corpus callosum removed.* f. *Removal of the hippocampus from the brain after the connections of the hippocampus to the fornix have been cut.*

core. Strip away fibers of the corpus callosum by tearing in a lateral direction a few fibers at a time. Laterally these commissural fibers intermingle with those of the internal capsule. Most of the association fibers have probably been torn away unintentionally while you were removing the cortical substance. Try to leave about a $\frac{1}{16}$-inch shell of corpus callosum over the top of the brain. At this stage your dissection should look something like Figure 1-7,*d*.

On the lateral aspect of the brain expose the outside of the internal capsule. Some of the gray matter that you dig out to expose the internal capsule is the putamen. The putamen is part of the corpus striatum. After the internal capsule is fully displayed, cut off the remaining fibers of the corpus callosum. You will find that the lateral ventricles of the brain are now uncovered. Your dissection should look something like Figure 1-7,*e*.

Locate the curved horn-like hippocampus. You may have noticed, as you were stripping away the corpus callosum, a midsagittal membrane extending between the callosum and the hippocampus. This is the septum pellucidum, which separates the lateral ventricles. The fornix originates from the site at which the two hippocampi join together. Cut the hippocampi apart with a scalpel and cut one hippocampus from the fornix, leaving the other attached. As shown in Figure 1-7,*f*, pull the separated hippocampus backwards, noting how it would extend into the temporal and pyriform lobes of an undissected brain. Try to visualize how the lateral ventricles would follow the surface of the hippocampus into the temporal lobe of an undissected brain. Examine the cut surface of the fornix and notice that it continues ventrally to the base of the forebrain.

Examine the structures on the side of the brain from which you have removed the hippocampus. You should recognize this as the anterior part of the brain stem. Locate again the inferior and superior colliculi, the thalamus, and the caudate nucleus.

EXAMINATION OF TRANSVERSE SECTIONS

If there is time and if there are extra brains available, your instructor may want to make coronal sections of the brain and review the structures you have previously dissected.

Place a brain on a cutting surface with the dorsal side up and, with a long sharp knife, make a series of transverse cuts through the brain, beginning at the frontal pole of the cerebral hemispheres. Continue sectioning until you are just past the inferior colliculus. Make the sections approximately $\frac{3}{16}$-inch thick.

By correlating what you now see in two dimensions with structures with which you are familiar from your previous three-dimensional dissection, locate the following structures on as many sections as you can:

corpus callosum	hypothalamic area
caudate nucleus	third ventricle
internal capsule	hippocampus
anterior commissure	fornix
optic chiasm	mammillary body
optic tract	cerebral peduncles
thalamus	cerebral aqueduct

Dissection and Examination of the Internal Structure of the Rat Brain

In this exercise you will review the general structure of the mammalian central nervous system by examining the rat brain.* The rat brain is, of course, much smaller than those you have previously studied. However, many features are very similar and, if you have carefully studied the ruminant brain, you should have little difficulty with the rat brain.

Because some important structures cannot be seen on the surface, it will be necessary for you to section the brain into thin slices to study the internal structure. It is also necessary to stain the sections, since it is not always possible to distinguish important structures on unstained sections. The methods of sectioning and staining presented here are quite rapid and simple but yet adequate for making most major structures of the brain visible. The stain colors the gray matter (cells) dark blue and leaves white matter (nerve fibers) white. Your instructor may have you prepare sections by other, more staisfactory techniques if time is available, or he may have you look at previously prepared sections.

DISSECTION OF THE BRAIN

On the rat brain trace the rhinal fissure, which is actually the only fissure or sulcus on the rat cerebral hemispheres (Figure 1-8,*a*). The other lines or creases

Suggestion to instructor: Rat brains are not ordinarily available commercially. It is suggested that they be removed from rats that have been terminated after experiments. These animals can usually be obtained from the laboratories of psychology or biology departments.

you see are the indentations of blood vessels. On the ventral surface find the olfactory tract, optic nerves, optic tract, mammillary body, and pyriform lobe (Figure 1-8,*b*). Remove the cerebellum by carefully cutting the cerebellar peduncles, first on one side and then on the other, and lifting off the cerebellum (Figure 1-9,*a*). Examine the fourth ventricle. Next pull away the thin layer of cerebral cortex, exposing the corpus callosum (Figure 1-9,*b*). Carefully cut the corpus callosum and pull it laterally. This exposes the underlying lateral ventricles and relatively large hippocampi (Figure 1-9,*c*). Examine the brain at this stage of the dissection under a stereomicroscope. Sever the attachments of one hippocampus from the fornix and pull it laterally (Figure 1-9,*d*). Do the same for the other hippocampus. On the exposed brain stem note the large superior colliculus, the inferior colliculus, the thalamus, and other structures shown in Figure 1-8,*d*. Fibers of the internal capsule are so intermingled with the caudate nucleus that these structures cannot be identified. If an extra brain is available, cut midsagittally and identify structures shown in Figure 1-8,*c*.

SECTIONING AND STAINING FOR EXAMINATION OF INTERNAL STRUCTURE

Begin with a new rat brain. Brains should have been fixed in formalin at least three or four days before staining is attempted. There is almost no maximum limit on the amount of time brains may be fixed before staining.

Mount the brain in a student microtome, with the

14

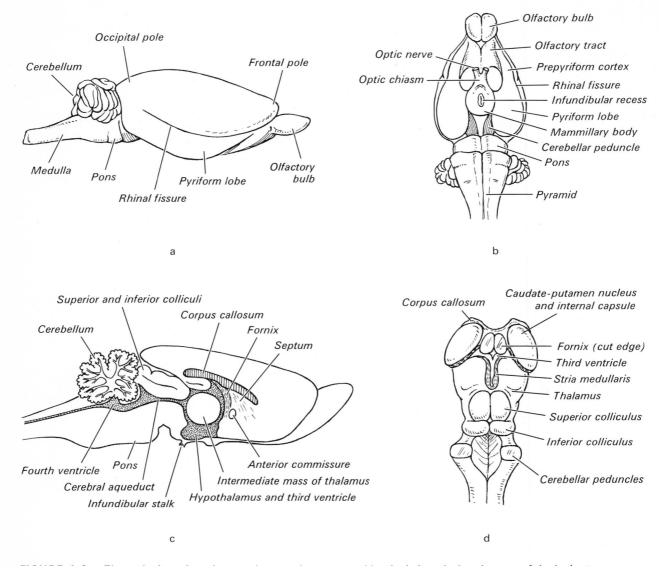

FIGURE 1-8. *The rat brain:* a. *lateral aspect;* b. *ventral aspect;* c. *midsagittal view;* d. *dorsal aspect of the brain stem.*

anterior portion of the brain exposed. Make sure the microtome adjustment and set screw are completely retracted. Cut off and discard the most anterior sections of the cerebral hemisphere where there is no corpus callosum holding the hemispheres together. Make appropriate adjustments of the microtome to cut sections of .5 to .7 mm in thickness. Make each cut with one complete diagonal motion, in order to obtain tissue sections of uniform thickness (Figure 1-10,*a*). Keep both the knife and the brain tissue wet to facilitate cutting. It is best to cut from the ventral side toward the dorsal side. Keep the sections in the proper sequence by placing them in tissue capsules that are numbered (Figure 1-10,*b*).

Once the brain sections have been placed in the numbered capsules, follow the staining procedures in

the order in which they are listed below. First check to make sure all solutions are available in sufficient quantity. Your instructor may have made up some of the solutions in advance.

1) Wash the sections, still enclosed in their capsules, in cold tap water for about 30 minutes (Figure 1-11,*a*).

2) Place the enclosed sections in a warm solution of phenol and copper sulfate for 5 minutes (50 g phenol, 5 g copper sulfate, and 1.25 ml concentrated HC1 per liter of solution). Maintain the temperature of the solution at 60°C by placing the dish of solution on a hot plate. The phenol solution applies a protective coating which inhibits the staining of the white matter. *Because inhalation of a strong concentration of fumes from the phenol*

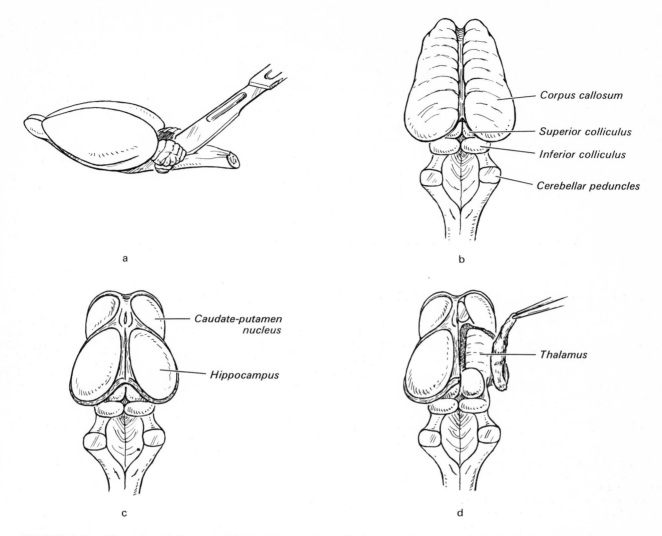

FIGURE 1-9. *Dissection of the cerebral hemispheres to the rat brain:* a. *cutting the cerebellar peduncles to remove the cerebellum;* b. *appearance of the brain with the cerebellum and cerebral cortex removed;* c. *appearance of the brain with the corpus callosum removed;* d. *removal of the hippocampus after the connections to the fornix have been cut.*

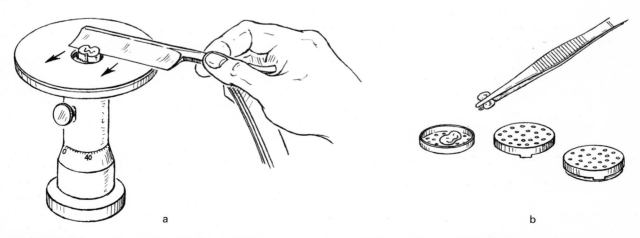

FIGURE 1-10. a. *Cut sections of a .5-mm thickness; use an even, uninterrupted cut and slide the blade as the cut is made.* b. *Place sections in numbered tissue capsules.*

solution may be harmful, it is best if the warm phenol solution is kept in a hood or near an open window (Figure 1-11,*b*).

3) Rinse the sections in ice water for 5 to 10 seconds; avoid rinsing for more than 10 seconds (Figure 1-11,*c*).

4) Pour freshly prepared 2% ferric chloride solution into a shallow dish or petri plate (Figure 1-11,*d*) and immerse the sections for 30 to 60 seconds in this solution (Figure 1-11,*e*).

5) Wash the sections for 2 to 3 minutes in cold tap water (Figure 1-11,*f*).

6) Remove the lids of the tissue capsules, so that the sections are visible, and immerse the sections in a freshly prepared 1% potassium ferrocyanide solution for about 5 minutes. The duration of time is not critical, but it is wise to remove the sections when the differential staining is optimal. The potassium ferrocyanide will react with the ferric chloride to form ferric ferrocyanide, which stains the gray matter blue (Figure 1-12,*g*).

7) Gently wash the individual sections in a beaker of tap water. If the gray matter is not stained a deep blue the sections, which have been washed in tap water, may be individually dipped again into a small container of 2% ferric chloride solution (step 4) until the gray matter turns deep blue. The moist sections should be placed between glass slides, 2 inches by 3 inches, so that drying is prevented (Figure 1-11,*h*). The staining in your sections should appear similar to those shown in Figure 1-12.

FIGURE 1-11. a. *Wash sections in tap water for 30 minutes.* b. *Place sections in a warm solution of phenol and copper sulfate for 5 minutes (in hood or near an open window).* c. *Rinse sections in ice water for 5 to 10 seconds.* d. *Pour freshly prepared ferric chloride solution into a shallow dish.* e. *Immerse sections in freshly prepared ferric chloride solution for 30 to 60 seconds.* f. *Wash sections in tap water for 2 to 3 minutes.* g. *With lids removed from tissue capsules, immerse sections for approximately 5 minutes in potassium ferrocyanide; remove sections when differential staining is optimal.* h. *Place stained brain sections between two glass slides (2 inches × 3 inches). Number the sections on the glass slides.* i. *View stained sections under a stereomicroscope.*

EXAMINATION OF STAINED SECTIONS

Beginning with sections at the anterior end of the brain and proceeding posteriorly, match each section as closely as possible with the photographs and illustrations in the stereotaxic atlas (Section 4). It is important that you identify the following structures or areas (listed anterior to posterior):

cerebral cortex
corpus callosum
caudate-putamen nuclei
anterior commissure
septal area
preoptic area
amygdaloid nuclei
stria medullaris
fornix
optic chiasm
anterior hypothalamic area
lateral hypothalamic area
internal capsule
thalamus
hippocampus
ventromediohypothalamic are a (nucleus)
columns of the fornix
mammillothalamic tract
habenular nuclei
cerebral peduncle
posterior hypothalamic area
mammillary nuclei
superior collicului
medial geniculate bodies

It would be wise for students to form small groups and quiz each other about various parts. Many structures may be seen with the unaided eye, but others will be best seen with a stereomicroscope (Figure 1-11,*i*). Try to correlate, as much as possible, the structures that you see on the transverse sections with the appearance of the surface of the brain stem. In sectioning, you may not have cut through some important structures so that these will be missed in your own sequence of sections. It will thus be necessary for you to observe the brain sections used by other students, or groups of students, in order to see all the structures. It is important to remember that the angle of cut you used in sectioning the brains is likely to be different than the angle of cut used for the sections illustrated in the stereotaxic atlas. Thus it will probably be necessary for you to use illustrations from several anterior-posterior planes in the atlas in order to identify all of the structures on your brain sections.

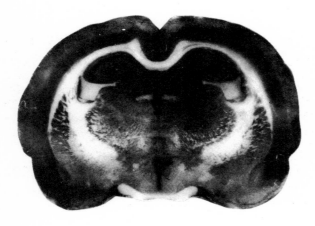

a

b

c

FIGURE 1-12. *Sections of the brain as they should appear following staining procedures:* a. *section through the caudate-putamen nucleus;* b. *section through the optic chiasm and middle thalamus;* c. *section through the posterior thalamus. The three levels are approximately those of A. 1.0, P. 2.0, and P. 4.0, respectively, of the stereotaxic atlas (Section 4).*

REFERENCES

Papez, J. W., 1929. *Comparative Neurology. A manual and text for the study of the nervous system.* New York, Hafner.

Zeman, W., and J. R. M. Innes, 1963. *Craigie's neuroanatomy of the rat.* New York, Academic Press.

SOURCES OF MATERIALS

Sources are not mentioned for such materials as laboratory glassware. These items, if they are not already on hand, are readily available from several general laboratory or biological supply houses. Items that instructors may have some difficulty finding are listed under either the category of materials needed by individual groups (2 to 4 students) or the category of materials that may be shared by two or more groups. Usually no more than four groups, and preferably fewer, should share a piece of equipment. When several sources are listed it would be best to obtain catalogs for all of them and choose the most suitable. The lists of sources are not, of course, necessarily complete.

MATERIALS NEEDED BY INDIVIDUAL GROUPS

Beef spinal cords ($15–$20 per dozen)
  SOURCES: Carolina, Turtox, Wards
Cow brains ($6–$12 each)
  SOURCES: Carolina, Turtox, Wards
Sheep brains ($3–$5 each)
  SOURCES: Carolina, Turtox, Wards
Human brains ($60–$70 each)
  SOURCES: Carolina, Turtox, Wards
Dissecting instruments: each team will need one each of a scalpel handle, tooth-tip thumb forceps, probe, scissors, and several scalpel blades ($10–$15 per set)
  SOURCES: Clay-Adams, Carolina, Turtox, Wards
Dissecting pan ($4–$6)
  SOURCES: Clay-Adams, Carolina, Turtox, Wards
Staining materials: each team will need several tissue capsules, petri dishes, and 2- x 3-inch glass slides ($5–$10 per set)
  SOURCES: Scientific Products, Van Waters and Rogers, Arthur H. Thomas

MATERIALS THAT CAN BE SHARED BY TWO OR MORE GROUPS

Student microtome ($12–$75)
  SOURCES: Carolina, Lafayette
Student stereomicroscope ($150–$400 each)
  SOURCES: Carolina, Clay-Adams, Turtox, Wards
Hot plates ($20–$60 each)
  SOURCES: Scientific Products, Van Waters and Rogers, Arthur H. Thomas

Staining chemicals: phenolcrystals, hydrochloric acid, ferric chloride, potassium ferrocyanide ($10–$30)
  SOURCES: Matheson, Coleman and Bell, Fisher, Mallinckroot (through Aloe)

COMMERCIAL ADDRESSES

Aloe Medical
  1831 Olive Street
  St. Louis, Missouri, 63103
Carolina Biological Supply Company
  Burlington, North Carolina 27216
Clay-Adams
  141 E. 25th Street
  New York, New York 10010
Fisher Scientific Company
  1458 N. Lamon Avenue
  Chicago, Illinois 60651
Lafayette Radio Electronics
  111 Jericho Turnpike
  Syosset, Long Island, New York 11791
Matheson, Coleman and Bell
  P.O. Box 85
  East Rutherford, New Jersey 07073
Scientific Products
  1210 Leon Place
  Evanston, Illinois 60201
Arthur H. Thomas Company
  Vine Street at Third
  P.O. Box 779
  Philadelphia, Pennsylvania 19105
Turtox Products
  General Biological Supply House
  8200 South Hoyne Avenue
  Chicago, Illinois 60620
Van Waters and Rogers
  P.O. Box 3200
  Rincon Annex
  San Francisco, California 94119
Ward's Natural Science Establishment, Inc.
  P.O. Box 1712
  Rochester, New York 14603
Ward's of California
  P.O. Box 1749
  Monterey, California 93942

PRINCIPLES OF STEREOTAXIC SURGERY

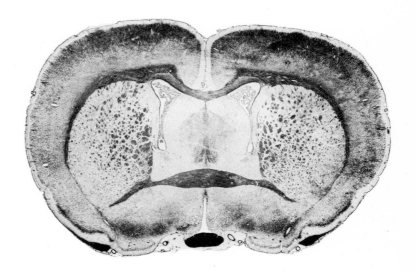

SECTION **2**

INTRODUCTION

Lesioning (destroying) small areas of the brain by electrocoagulation or by heat, and implanting electrodes or cannulae into the brain so that it can be electrically or chemically stimulated at a later time require stereotaxic surgery and the use of a stereotaxic instrument.

In this section you will be introduced to experimental techniques used in stereotaxic surgery. The principle of stereotaxic surgery is based upon the constant relationship between the surface of the skull and the parts of the brain. Three systems of coordinates—anteroposterior, vertical, and lateral—are used to guide an electrode into a given location in the brain, which has been determined by referring to landmarks on the skull surface. The techniques include the preparation of electrodes and anesthetization of the rat, which will be introduced in Parts A and B. Parts C and D are exercises in actual stereotaxic work. It is highly recommended that you do these two exercises the first time on dead rats or on heads of previously frozen or dead rats: if you do so,

you will be able to take your time without having to be concerned with problems of sterile technique, anesthetic level, or hemorrhage. Also, suture lines of the skull, which are used as stereotaxic landmarks, show up more clearly on the heads of dead animals.

In Part E you will learn how to perfuse and remove the brain so that at a later date the brain can be sectioned and stained to determine which parts were lesioned or stimulated.

The techniques described in this section are routinely used in neuropsychological experiments on the laboratory rat, but not necessarily on other laboratory animals. For example, in most animals it is sometimes preferable to administer fluid or drugs in veins; however, in the rat, blood vessels are either too small or too inaccessible and, therefore, alternative routes are used. In addition to some of the materials and instruments you used in Section 1, you will need other items, which are listed in the *Sources of Materials* at the end of this section.

Preparation of Monopolar Electrodes

Monopolar electrodes are used when the experimenter desires either to lesion or to stimulate the brain by passing current between the relatively small exposed area of the tip of the electrode and a ground or reference terminal that is a contact with a relatively large amount of body tissue. In this way current is "focused" at the tip of the electrode. In making lesions the monopolar electrode is usually connected to the anode (positive terminal) of the current source. Attaching the monopolar electrode to the cathode (negative terminal) would result in the formation of gas bubbles in the tissue around the electrode tip.

Bipolar electrodes are used frequently in stimulation experiments and occasionally in making lesions. Current is passed between the tips of two electrodes that are twisted or glued together. The area stimulated or lesioned by bipolar electrodes is more circumscribed than the area affected by monopolar electrodes. Because bipolar electrodes are more difficult to prepare than monopolar electrodes and are commercially available, instructions for their preparation are not given in this manual.

Several types of materials, including small-gauge hypodermic needles, straight suturing needles, and metal wire or tubing may be used for constructing electrodes. Stainless steel has one disadvantage: when electrical current is passed through it iron deposits are left in the tissue and may, in a few instances, excite neutrons in the immediate area. For this reason electrodes made of platinum tubing (with 10% iridium) are probably the best. However, since iron deposition does not affect the results of the experiments in this manual and platinum tubing is expensive, students may use stainless steel insect pins of size 00,

which are inexpensive and make quite satisfactory electrodes.

LESION ELECTRODES

Use a stainless steel wire, pin, or tubing that is approximately 40 mm long. If you are using an insect pin and if there is a small bead on top of the pin, pull it off with pliers. Apply one or two coats of insulation to the electrode (Figure 2-1,a). A satisfactory and durable insulation is "Epoxylite" varnish, which must be cured in a home oven for approximately an hour (follow the directions supplied with the varnish). You can use bent paper clips to hang electrodes from a rack in the oven (Figure 2-1,b). Avoid coating the top of the electrode. After the varnish has cured or dried, the top 3 mm of the electrode should be bent at a right angle so that miniature alligator clips can be attached to the electrode before it is lowered into the brain. The bottom tip of the pin should then be snipped off with wire cutters and approximately .5 mm of the insulation should be scraped from the electrode tip with a scalpel (Figure 2-1,c). It is best to do this under a stereomicroscope, using a small metric ruler as a guide.

Before mounting the electrode in the electrode carrier of the stereotaxic instrument, be sure to check the continuity of the electrode insulation by examining the integrity of the insulation with an ohmmeter according to your instructor's directions or examine the insulation under a stereomicroscope. If the surface is scratched or nicked, this means that a portion of the electrode, other than the tip, may contact

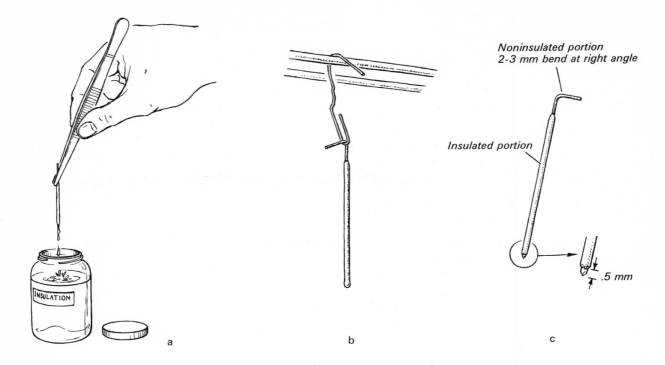

FIGURE 2-1. a. *Dip the electrodes into insulation, leaving the top part of the electrode bare; drawing the electrode out slowly results in a thinner coat.* b. *Electrodes may be cured in the oven, using a bent paper clip as a holder.* c. *Finished electrode for lesioning brain.*

brain tissue so that, when current is passed, a lesion may be produced somewhere along electrode track as well as at the tip of the electrode. For this reason, discard any electrode in which the insulation is cracked, chipped, or scratched. Also, before using an electrode that has been previously used on another animal, check not only the insulation, but the tip of the electrode as well, to be sure that tissue has not adhered to the tip; this will disrupt the even flow of the current. If there is old, dried blood or brain tissue on the tip, scrape the tip again with a scalpel. If necessary, snip a portion of the tip from the electrode and scrape another .55 mm from the tip.

ELECTRODES FOR IMPLANTATION

Use a stainless steel wire, pin, or tubing about 40 mm long. If you are using an insect pin, and if there is a small bead on the top of the pin, pull it off with pliers. Solder a strand of uninsulated copper wire, approximately 30-gauge, onto the electrode about 7 mm down from the top. Leave about 1 cm of the copper wire attached to the pin and apply a ball of solder to the tip of the wire. This can be done by dipping the copper wire into a molten ball of solder dropped onto a table. If you are not experienced with soldering this

may take some practice. To get the solder to hold to stainless steel you may have to roughen the stainless steel with sandpaper (also use acid soldering flux). It is extremely important that the soldered connections be electrically sound. If you are in doubt twist the wire against the electrode; if the solder connection

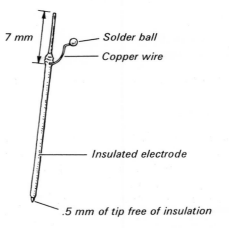

FIGURE 2-2. *The finished electrode for implantation into the skull. Note that the electrode should be dipped into insulation up to the point at which the copper wire is soldered onto the electrode.*

breaks easily it was not electrically sound.

Apply a coat of insulation to the electrode just past the point at which the copper wire is attached. If "Epoxylite" insulation is used it can be cured in the oven by hanging the electrode in a paper clip.

When you are preparing to implant the electrode, calculate the vertical distance from the top of the skull to the ultimate location of the tip of the electrode. Add an additional 2 mm and measure this distance from the bottom of the attachment of the copper wire to the electrode and snip off the end of the electrode at this point. Then scrape about .5 mm of the insulation from the electrode tip with a scalpel. Depending upon the type of neuropsychological experiment you will be doing, your instructor may specify that the tip not be scraped so that the spread of the electrical current can be decreased. When this electrode is implanted, the junction of the copper wire to the electrode will be about 2 mm above the surface of the skull. The finished electrode should look like Figure 2-2.

Just before mounting the electrode in the electrode carrier, check the continuity of the insulation of the electrode and discard any in which the insulation is cracked, chipped, or scratched. Also, before the electrode is mounted in the electrode carrier the copper wire should be bent so that the solder bead will end up just above the surface of the acrylic plastic pedestal. In a subsequent period, miniature alligator clips can be attached to the solder ball on the copper wire so that a small current can be delivered to the brain of the animal.

Anesthetization of the Rat

The most generally satisfactory method of anesthetizing the rat for neurological surgery is with an intraperitoneal (intra-abdominal) injection of a barbiturate anesthetic. Ether anesthesia may be desirable for some surgical procedures if it is administered very carefully, but it's disadvantages are that it is an explosive hazard and that the level of anesthesia has to be monitored constantly.

When an animal is given an anesthetizing dose of an injectable anesthetic it goes through several stages of anesthetic depth before reaching the level at which surgery can be started. The animal goes through these stages more slowly when the anesthetic is injected intraperitoneally than it does if the injection is intravenous, and usually about twenty minutes are required for a rat to become fully anesthetized from an intraperitoneal injection. For humane reasons and for best experimental results you will have to make certain that the animal is fully unconscious before surgery is begun. Your instructor may want you to administer a small amount of atropine (15 mg) to suppress salivation and to reduce the possibility of the animal aspirating saliva during surgery.

ANESTHETIC DOSE

The most commonly used barbiturate is sodium pentobarbital. A dose of 5 mg per 100 g for females of any weight as well as for males under 300 g is generally sufficient, and 6 mg per 100 g is usually enough for males weighing more than 300 g. A dose of 8 mg per 100 g may be lethal for some rats.

After a few minutes the effects of the anesthetic can be seen and after about 10 minutes the rat should lie motionless. In about 20 minutes, if the dose has been sufficient, the animal should be ready for surgery. The level of anesthesia may be tested by noting the presence or absence of certain reflexes, such as leg withdrawal (flexion reflex) when the toe is pinched, or head twitching when the ear is pinched.

The anesthetic tables will be a useful reference for determining the total amount of anesthetic needed when sodium pentobarbital in the strength of either 65 mg per ml (commercial strength) or 16.25 mg per ml (one-fourth commercial strength) is used. For rats weighing less than 300 g, it is best to use the more dilute concentration of anesthetic. The anesthetic dose for the weight of your particular rat may be extrapolated from the tables.

INJECTING THE ANESTHETIC

First weigh the rat (Figure 2-3,a). Then wipe the top of the anesthetic vial with a gauze sponge soaked with alcohol. Use a sterile 1-cc or 2-cc syringe with a 22-gauge $\frac{1}{2}$-inch needle. Fill the syringe with as much (or more) air as is needed to replace the fluid withdrawn from the vial. Inject the air into the vial and immediately withdraw the amount of solution needed (Figure 2-3,b).

You may restrain a rat for an intraperitoneal injection by holding its tail in one hand, grasping its thorax in your other hand, and pushing the front

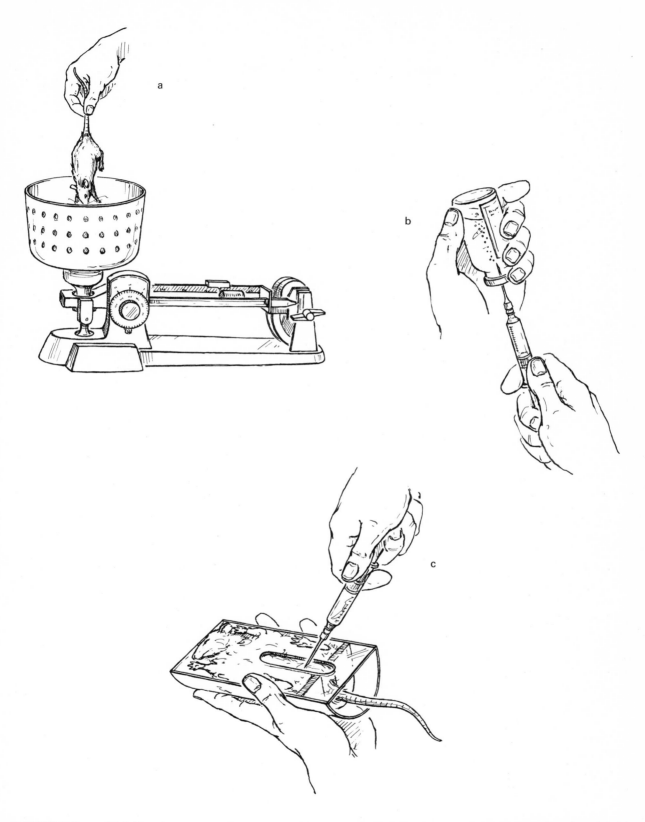

FIGURE 2-3.   a. *Weighing the rat.* b. *To fill syringe wipe off top of vial with alcohol and then inject enough air into the vial to approximate the amount of solution to be withdrawn.* c. *After the rat has been coaxed into the restrainer, quickly turn it over and inject the calculated amount of anesthetic.*

legs towards its head to prevent it from biting. Another individual then injects the anesthetic. Use of a glass cylinder or a restraining device, such as the one shown in Figure 2-3,*c*, is safer and makes it possible for one person to administer the anesthetic. If such a restraining device is available, coax the rat in through the open end and quickly insert the syringe and inject the anesthetic.

Make an intraperitoneal injection by grasping the hair or skin on the abdomen and pushing the needle through the skin and muscle of the abdominal wall. You must make certain that the needle is pushed completely through the abdominal muscles. A subcutaneous injection (between skin and abdominal muscles) will cause absorption of the anesthetic to be very slow, and the animal may become only sedated rather than anesthetized. Insert the needle 1 inch below the rib cage in order to avoid injecting into the stomach or liver. You need not worry about hitting the intestines because these organs have little resistance and are easily pushed aside as the needle enters the abdominal cavity.

SUPPLEMENTARY DOSES

Frequently, because of individual differences, the calculated dose of barbiturate anesthetic is not sufficient. If it is not, the rat will not have lost consciousness within twenty minutes after the initial dose. Also, if a surgical procedure is extended the animal may begin to recover before surgery is completed. In either case, it may be desirable to administer a supplementary dose. Inject a supplementary dose of sodium pentobarbital that is equivalent to the 2 mg per 100 g of body weight indicated in the anesthetic tables. Wait 15 to 20 minutes and, if more is needed, repeat the dose. Your instructor may want you to use chloral hydrate as a supplementary dose because of its wide safety margin. The first supplementary dose of chloral hydrate should be 0.1 cc of a 300 mg per ml concentration. If two supplementary doses do not satisfactorily anesthetize your rat, it is probably best to put him aside and use another rat. The first rat can then be used another time, but it would be given a larger initial dose of anesthetic.

TABLE 2-1 Anesthetic Table for 65 mg per ml Concentration

Total Volume in Millimeters of Sodium Pentobarbital Solution
to be Administered to Rat Intraperitoneally

Weight of Rat in Grams	Dosage Level			
	2 mg per 100 g body weight (supplementary dose)	5 mg per 100 g body weight	6 mg per 100 g body weight	7 mg per 100 g body weight
100	.03	.07	.09	.11
150	.05	.11	.14	.16
200	.06	.15	.18	.22
250	.08	.19	.23	.27
300	.09	.23	.28	.32
350	.11	.27	.32	.38
400	.12	.31	.37	.43
450	.14	.35	.42	.48
500	.15	.39	.46	.54
550	.17	.43	.51	.59
600	.18	.47	.55	.65
650	.20	.51	.60	.70
700	.22	.55	.65	.75

TABLE 2-2 Anesthetic Table for 16.25 mg per ml Concentration

Total Volume in Millimeters of Sodium Pentobarbital Solution
to be Administered to Rat Intraperitoneally

Weight of Rat in Grams	Dosage Level			
	2 mg per 100 g body weight (supplementary dose)	5 mg per 100 g body weight	6 mg per 100 g body weight	7 mg per 100 g body weight
100	.12	.30	.36	.42
150	.18	.45	.55	.64
200	.24	.61	.73	.85
250	.30	.76	.91	1.06
300	.36	.91	1.09	1.27
350	.42	1.06	1.27	1.48
400	.47	1.21	1.46	1.70
450	.53	1.36	1.64	1.91
500	.59	1.51	1.82	2.12
550	.65	1.67	2.00	2.33
600	.71	1.82	2.18	2.54
650	.77	1.97	2.36	2.76
700	.83	2.12	2.54	2.97

Stereotaxic Surgery: Placing Lesions in the Brain

Become well acquainted with the particular stereotaxic instrument you will be using. Several stereotaxic instruments are available. Two examples are shown in Figure 2-4. Your instructor will show you how to use the electrode carrier adjustment, the vernier scales, and how to mount the electrode in the electrode carrier for your instrument. On some stereotaxic instruments the electrode carrier can be moved aside to allow more room for surgical procedures. Refer to the stereotaxic atlas (Section 4) to determine the proper tilt of the skull and to obtain the coordinates of the structure in which you wish to place an electrode. When a nucleus or other structure extends for several transverse planes it is best to calculate an electrode position that is in the approximate middle of the anterior and posterior extents of the structure. It is suggested that you go through the entire procedure of lesioning the brain on the head of a dead rat.

Surgery on the head is easier than surgery on other parts of the body. Usually there is little or no danger of excessive hemorrhage and, since the surgical area is easily exposed, there is usually no problem with adequate lighting. A major advantage in using the laboratory rat is its resistance to infection caused by bacterial contamination. Therefore absolute disinfection of the skin, and sterilization of surgical instruments or suture material are not critical. Nevertheless the skin should be as sterile as possible and you should scrub your hands well before surgery. Surgical instruments should be cold-sterilized in a disinfectant solution or sterilized in a steam sterilizer.

Be sure the animal is deeply anesthetized before beginning to prepare the skin for surgery or before placing the head in the stereotaxic frame.

PREPARATION OF THE SKIN FOR SURGERY

The animal's skin may be prepared either before or after the head is placed in a stereotaxic frame. Since its eyes may be exposed for a prolonged period of time it is advisable to protect the cornea of the eye by placing a drop of mineral oil in each eye after the animal is anesthetized.

With electric clippers or scissors clip the hair from the top of the head. Start at the back and clip to the site just behind the eyes. Be careful not to nick the ears. If you have used scissors, you may have to shave the center of the clipped area with a safety razor or scalpel blade. When the animal's head is in the stereotaxic frame, wipe the clipped or shaved skin lightly with a gauze sponge dampened with alcohol, being extremely careful not to get any alcohol in the animal's eyes.

PLACEMENT OF THE HEAD IN THE STEREOTAXIC FRAME

On most stereotaxic instruments the head is fixed in three places, the two bony ear canals and the upper jaw. If a rat's skull* is available, practice positioning

---

*Rat skulls may be purchased (see *Sources of Materials* at the end of this section) or prepared from rat heads by defleshing with the use of dermestid beetles. See E. J. Coleman and J. R.A Zbijewska, "Defleshing of Skulls by Beetles," *Turtox News* **46**, 204–205, 1968.

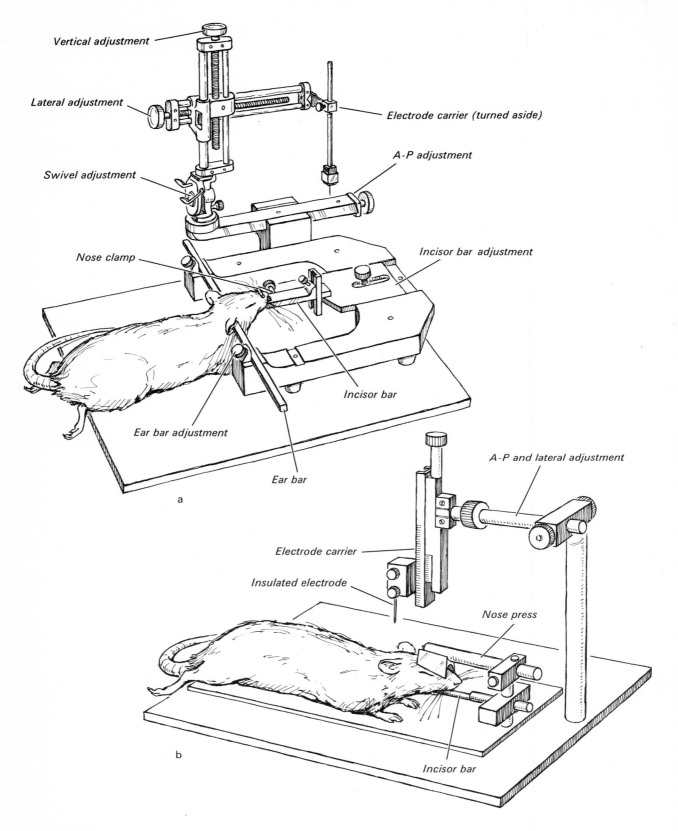

Vertical adjustment

Lateral adjustment

Swivel adjustment

Nose clamp

Ear bar adjustment

Ear bar

Electrode carrier (turned aside)

A-P adjustment

Incisor bar adjustment

Incisor bar

a

A-P and lateral adjustment

Electrode carrier

Insulated electrode

Nose press

Incisor bar

b

FIGURE 2-4.   a. *A stereotaxic instrument with ear bars and adjustable incisor bar; the rat is properly positioned.* b. *A stereotaxic instrument without ear bars.*

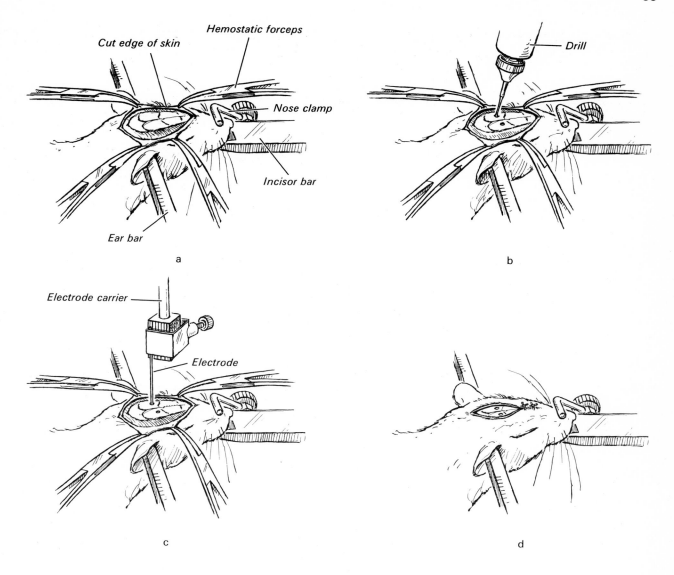

FIGURE 2-5. *Making a bilateral lesion: a. skull exposed; b. bilateral holes drilled in calculated position; c. electrode inserted to calculated depth; d. suturing skin.*

it in the frame. Insert the ear bars into the ear canal on each side. Notice that when the ear bars are properly placed the skull pivots freely about the axis of the ear canal, but that there is very little lateral movement of the skull. Adjust the incisor bar and nose clamp on the skull and note how this adjustment determines the tilt of the skull and brain. The incisor bar should then be gently retracted anteriorly and securely tightened.

Next take the head (of a dead rat, the first time) and position it in the stereotaxic instrument by first placing the ear bars into the bony ear canals. You should be able to palpate the bony orifice. Fit the ear bars snugly against the skull. Center the head in the middle of the stereotaxic frame and tighten the ear bars. Like the skull, the head should pivot freely about the axis of the ear canals but it should have very little lateral movement. Some investigators slit the skin just in front of the ear over the bony ear canal to facilitate insertion of the ear bars. If your instructor wants you to use this procedure he will probably demonstrate the technique. Move the incisor bar so that it is under and behind the upper incisors. Position the nose clamp over the nose, and then gently pull back on the incisor bar to tighten it. You can move the head by releasing the nose clamp, the incisor bar, and then the ear bars. It is important that you practice positioning the head several times.

TABLE 2-3 Sample Calculations for Bilateral Electrode Placement

	Coordinates from Atlas (Ventromedial hypothalamic nucleus)	Instrument Zero Point Readings	Readings for Final Electrode Placement
A-P	P 2.5 mm	70.1 mm	67.6 mm
Lateral	± 0.6 mm	22.6 mm	22 and 23.2 mm
Vertical	8.4 mm	20.4 mm	12.0 mm

INCISING THE SKIN AND EXPOSING THE SKULL

Start with a clean sharp scalpel blade. Hold the skin tightly on the sides of the head and make a midline incision with a long stroke of the scalpel blade, using firm pressure so that the skin is completely incised with the first stroke. The result is a straight wound edge. When the skin is sutured, a straight wound edge heals more quickly than a jagged wound edge, which is produced by passing the scalpel over the incision several times. After the skin is incised it is best to dissect the skin bluntly from the skull with scissors. In larger animals, blood vessels in the skin are usually clamped off with hemostatic forceps, but this is unnecessary for the rat because there is usually very little hemorrhage from the skin. The skin flaps should be held aside by hemostatic forceps. These forceps should be clamped on the inside of the skin flap. Try to grab only the loose subcutaneous tissue on the inside of the skin so that you do not damage the skin by pinching it.

After the skull is exposed it will be necessary to scrape the periosteum or bone covering from the top of the skull with a scalpel in order to see the skull suture lines and to facilitate drilling holes in the skull. If the periosteum is not removed it will clog the cutting edges of the bone drill. When the periosteum is removed, blood vessels in the skull may start bleeding. This hemorrhage can be stopped by applying pressure with clean cotton or gauze for about 2 minutes. If an air hose is available, bone hemorrhage can also be stopped with a small jet of air directed to the source of bleeding. Wipe the top of the skull with clean gauze pads. When the skull has dried, the coronal suture, the sagittal suture, and the bregma will be prominent. Identify these skull landmarks by referring to the stereotaxic atlas.

POSITIONING THE ELECTRODE

It is assumed that you will be using the stereotaxic atlas of Section 4; thus, unless your instructor advises you otherwise, follow the instructions below for positioning the electrode.

When the electrode is in the electrode carrier (Figure 2-6), adjust the carrier so that the electrode is directly above the bregma. Take readings for the anteroposterior (A-P) and lateral zero points from the stereotaxic instrument. Calculate what the readings must be after the distances given in the stereotaxic atlas are added or subtracted from the A-P and lateral zero readings (see example below). Move the electrodes to the newly calculated A-P and lateral positions, and lower the electrode until it is just touching the skull. Take a vertical zero reading and then calculate what the final reading must be in order for the electrode to penetrate the brain to the specified depth. Table 2-3 shows a sample calculation for all three coordinates for a bilateral electrode placement.

When the electrode is in the newly calculated position, raise the electrode a few millimeters and mark, with a sharp pencil, the point on the skull directly below the electrode tip. Move the electrode aside and, using an electric drill, drill a hole in the skull at the points indicated by the pencil mark (Figure 2-5). When the hole has been drilled in the skull, the electrode should again be positioned in the A-P and lateral planes, over the hole according to previous cal-

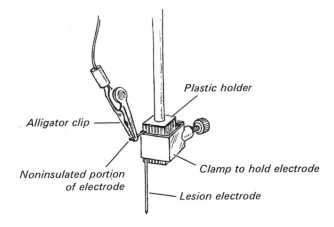

Alligator clip

Noninsulated portion of electrode

Plastic holder

Clamp to hold electrode

Lesion electrode

FIGURE 2-6. *Position of lesion electrode in electrode carrier.*

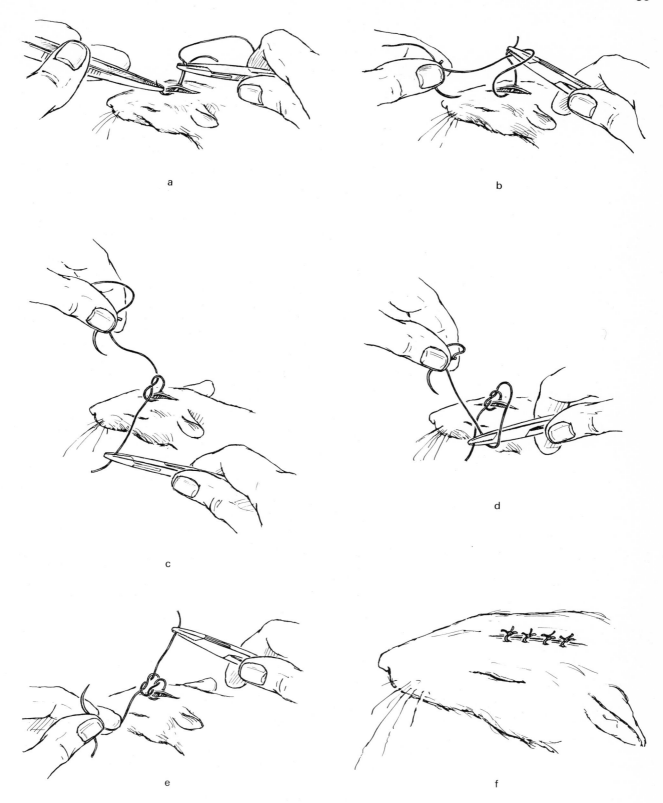

FIGURE 2-7. *Suturing skin with the instrument tie: a. push the cutting-edge needle through both edges of the skin;*
b. loop the needle end of thread around needle holder, grasp the free end of the thread, and pull through for the first overhand
tie; c. gently tighten the first overhand tie; d. make the second overhand tie in the reverse direction of the first overhand tie;
e. tighten the second overhand tie to complete the square knot; f. sutures should be placed about ⅜ inch apart.

culations. Next lower the electrode the required number of millimeters to the reading for the vertical electrode placement (Figure 2-5,c). Be sure that the electrodes are straight before they are inserted, and be careful that the electrode does not strike the bone as it is being lowered, because contact with the bone will cause it to deviate from the desired position. If the electrode does not pass freely into the hole, the hole should be enlarged.

MAKING ELECTROLYTIC LESIONS

Your instructor will show you how to operate the particular lesion-making instrument you are using. With the electrode in position, the lead from the anode (+) of an electrolytic lesion-maker should be clamped to the top of the electrode, where the insulation has been removed (Figure 2-6). Be careful that the clip on the anodal head (+) does not touch any metal part of the stereotaxic instrument, or that attaching the lead does not deflect the electrode. The lead from the cathode (−) is clamped to some other part of the animal such as the exposed muscle on the side of the skull. The amount of current used to make the lesion will vary depending upon the experiment being conducted. If you are practicing with a dead animal, you might pass current of 1 milliampere (ma) for 30 seconds. After all lesions are made, remove the electrodes and wash them with water.

SUTURING THE SKIN

The manner in which skin is sutured determines the speed of healing. Several different knots and methods of suturing are used, depending upon the type of skin and the location of the wound on the body. The suture that should be used in closing the skin of the skull is the simple interrupted suture, which is actually just a square knot. It is necessary to hold the skin while suturing, and, for this, the so-called rat-tooth or mouse-tooth thumb forceps are the most convenient. The skin may slip through forceps that are only serrated. A curved ($\frac{3}{8}$- or $\frac{1}{2}$-inch curve) cutting-edge needle is needed for suturing skin. Use silk suture material of 00 gauge, which has been cut into lengths of about 6 inches. Simple interrupted sutures should be placed about 3 mm apart.

The most efficient and rapid way of suturing skin on top of the head, where working space is limited, is with the instrument tie, which involves the use of the needle holder to make two overhand ties into a square knot. The instrument tie is illustrated step-by-step in Figure 2-7,a-f. You might practice the technique on pieces of cloth before attempting it on animal skin. When you are suturing skin, remember not to pull the skin too tight: this is a very common mistake made by students and it may greatly retard healing of the edges of the skin. The skin should be drawn together so that the edges of the skin are just in contact. The first overhand tie is the most important in determining how tight the suture will be. The second overhand tie, forming the square knot, usually pulls the skin a little tighter. If a suture looks too tight, cut it out and begin again.

ADMINISTRATION OF ANTIBIOTIC

After surgery it is usually advisable to inject the animal with a single dose of antibiotic. The most frequently used antibiotic is penicillin (of either prolonged or short-term effect) or a combination of penicillin and streptomycin. The dose required is usually 0.1 cc of the commercially available strength. It should be injected into a muscle mass so that absorption is slow. The thigh muscle is the most convenient muscle mass for injection. Use a 22-gauge needle. It is advisable to push the needle through the (tough) skin first and then slowly into the muscle in order to avoid hitting the bone. Penicillin should be kept in the refrigerator when not in use.

Stereotaxic Surgery: Implanting Electrodes

The initial procedures of this exercise are very similar to those of Part C. The problem in implanting an electrode for electrical stimulation of the brain is stabilizing the electrode on the skull so that it will not move within the brain when the animal is conscious and moving about. Since there are no touch or pain receptors within the brain, animals cannot feel that there is an electrode implanted within it. If possible practice first with the head from a dead rat.

IMPLANTING MONOPOLAR ELECTRODES

After making certain the animal is fully anesthetized, follow the procedures in Part C for positioning the head, determining final electrode placements, and drilling a hole in the skull to insert an electrode (Figure 2-8,a). For the implantation procedure it is imperative that all the periosteum is removed from the exposed skull so that the acrylic dental cement will adhere to the skull. In addition to a hole for the electrode, drill holes for the insertion of one or two small screws that will anchor an acrylic plastic pedestal onto the rat's skull. The hole for the screw must be slightly smaller than the screw and should be drilled anterior or posterior to the electrode position but away from the sagittal suture.

Tightly twist a piece of 30-gauge copper wire with a ball of solder attached around one of the screws. Also twist around the same screw a piece of stainless steel wire. This screw will be used as the indifferent, or reference, electrode.

Next twist the reference screw into the skull (it should not penetrate the cortex) and thread the stain-less steel wire into muscle or subcutaneous tissue of the head. Lower an electrode (Figure 2-9) into the calculated position so that the tip lies in the structures to be stimulated (Figure 2-8,b). You may have to experiment with the position of the electrode carrier. If you use electrodes like those discussed in Part A, you will have to determine the position of the copper wires before actually inserting the electrode and anchoring it to the skull. If the copper wire is twisted after the electrode is anchored it may break the seal of acrylic dental cement to the skull.

Prepare a small amount of acrylic dental cement by mixing a bit of powder with the liquid on a watch glass. This is best done by making a mound of powder with a depression in the middle and dropping the liquid into the depression. Mix until the cement has the consistency of a heavy syrup or paste; you may have to experiment with mixing the cement before you actually mix some for the pedestal. Apply a small amount of the cement around the screws and electrode. The skull should be as dry as possible so that the cement will adhere to the skull. Apply two or three layers of cement. Use small amounts of cement and allow each layer to set (but it need not harden) before applying additional layers. A stream of air from a small air jet may be used for drying the skull and for helping to mold the cement. After the cement is hard, raise the electrode carrier after first releasing the clamp that holds the electrode to the carrier. Another electrode may also be inserted in the holder, and positioned in the brain, if there is working space (Figure 2-8,d). Each electrode should also be secured with one or two layers of cement. Build up a mound of cement, a little at a time, until the cement slightly

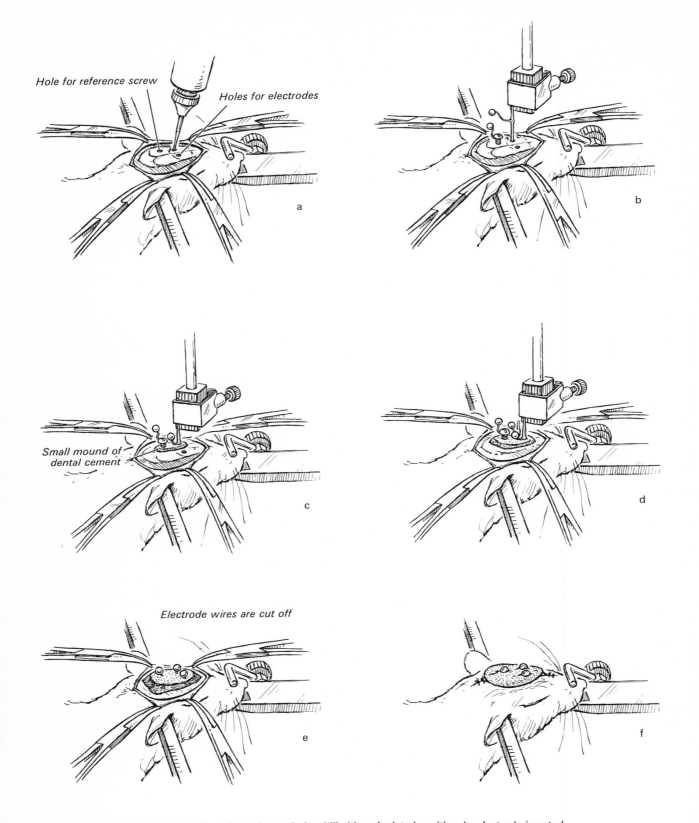

FIGURE 2-8. *Steps in implanting electrodes: a. holes drilled in calculated position; b. electrode inserted; c. application of dental cement to anchor the electrode before removing the electrode carrier; d. second electrode inserted and anchored by cement; e. building up mound of dental cement; f. suturing skin around finished pedestal.*

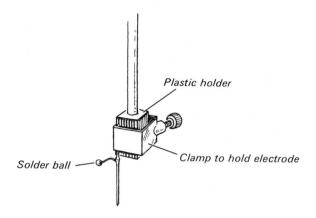

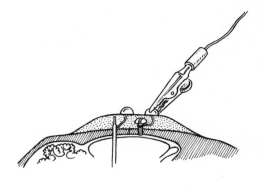

FIGURE 2-9. *Position of electrode in electrode carrier for implantation of electrode.*

FIGURE 2-10. *Cross-section of a plastic pedestal showing implanted electrode and indifferent electrode.*

covers the bottom of the solder-ball electrode terminals (Figure 2-8,*c*). When the cement has hardened and the animal's head has been removed from the instrument, the tops of the electrodes should be cut off carefully. A cross section of an acrylic plastic pedestal is illustrated in Figure 2-10.

SUTURING THE SKIN

Suture the anterior and posterior portions of the skin with simple interrupted sutures (see Part C). Sutures should be alternately placed anterior and posterior to the pedestal. Avoid pulling the skin too tightly around the pedestal (Figure 2-8,*f*).

IMPLANTING BIPOLAR ELECTRODES

Bipolar electrodes, most of which are prepared commercially, are implanted into the brain by a technique similar to that used with monopolar electrodes. However, a miniature electrode connector is often attached to the skull and the electrode wires are led into the connector. The miniature connectors are attached to the skull with screws and acrylic plastic cement. If you will be using bipolar electrodes or miniature electrical connectors your instructor will provide you with instructions for using the particular types you have.

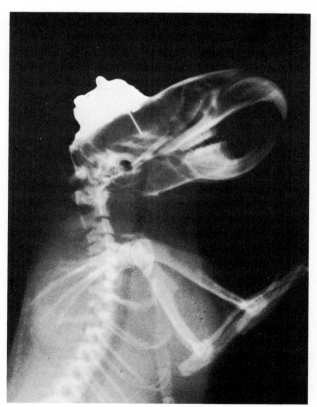

FIGURE 2-11. *X-ray of rat with implanted electrode in place. Note the pedestal of dental cement that secures the electrode.*

Perfusion and Removal of the Brain

In most experimental work on the brain it is necessary to examine the brain after the animal has been tested, to see exactly where lesions were made or electrodes implanted. When experimental animals are terminated, the brain, like other tissue in the body decomposes rapidly after death. Such decomposition makes the tissue difficult to handle and stain properly. Thus, if areas that were lesioned are to be examined to determine which structures of the brain were actually affected, it is necessary to "fix" the brain soon after death in order to prevent decomposition. Since brain tissue is very dense, the only way in which the fixative can reach the interior aspects rapidly is if the fixative is pumped through the arteries that supply the brain. This is done by first flushing blood out with physiological saline and then running formalin fixative (10%) into the blood vessels. This procedure is referred to as perfusion. Blood coagulates in the arteries and veins very soon after death and, therefore, it is best to begin the saline flush while the animal is deeply anesthetized rather than dead. This is a perfectly humane manner of sacrificing the experimental animal.

PERFUSION OF THE BRAIN

Your instructor should explain the use of the perfusion apparatus before you begin this procedure. A convenient apparatus is that shown in Figure 2-12,a.

Inject about twice the amount of barbiturate anesthetic needed for surgical anesthesia. After the animal is deeply anesthetized, cut through the abdominal muscles and into the thorax with scissors or a scalpel to expose the heart. Insert the perfusion needle into the apex, or tip, of the heart and into the left ventricle (Figure 2-12,b). Next, clamp a hemostatic forceps onto the point at which the needle enters the heart, so the needle will remain in place. Cut into the right atrium to allow blood to be drained from the head. Run saline into the heart until the fluid flowing from the right atrium becomes clear (about 300 ml) and then begin perfusing with 10% formalin. Run about 300 ml of formalin into the heart. Although the animal is dead at this point, you may notice a good deal of muscle twitching as it is perfused. When muscles are firm you can assume the perfusion is complete. This procedure actually perfuses not only the brain, but the entire animal.

REMOVAL OF THE BRAIN

Place the perfused rat in a dissecting pan and, with a scalpel, make an incision laterally from behind the ears to the front of the jaw as shown in Figure 2-13,a. Reflect the skin from the point of the incision behind the ears, and cut it away from the head down to the base of the nose (Figure 2-13,b). Scrape the periosteum from the surface of the skull and remove the temporal muscle from the cranium and the first two cervical vertebrae (Figure 2-13,c). When the skull has thus been exposed begin removing the cranial bone with small rongeurs or bone cutters. Crack the nasal bone just anteriorly to the eye sockets and chip away the cranium (Figure 2-13,d), bit-by-bit, until the brain is sufficiently uncovered that you are able to pry it out of the base of the skull (Figure 2-13,c). Be-

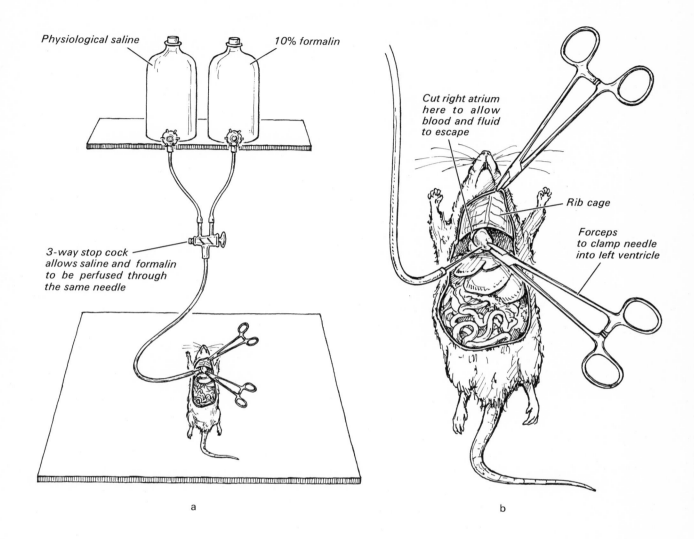

FIGURE 2-12.   a. *Perfusion apparatus. Use about 300 cc of physiological saline and 300 cc of formalin. b. Inserting the needle into the left ventricle to begin perfusion.*

fore starting to remove the brain, cut the dura from the surface of the cerebral hemispheres and cerebellum.

To remove the brain, first lift the anterior part, and as the cranial nerves are exposed cut them with fine scissors to avoid tearing the brain. Lift the rest of the brain from the skull and cut the upper part of the spinal cord to free the brain of its posterior connection (Figure 2-13,*f*). Place the brain in a small jar of 10% formalin so that fixation will continue. The brain should remain in fixative 3 or 4 days before sectioning and staining are attempted.

42

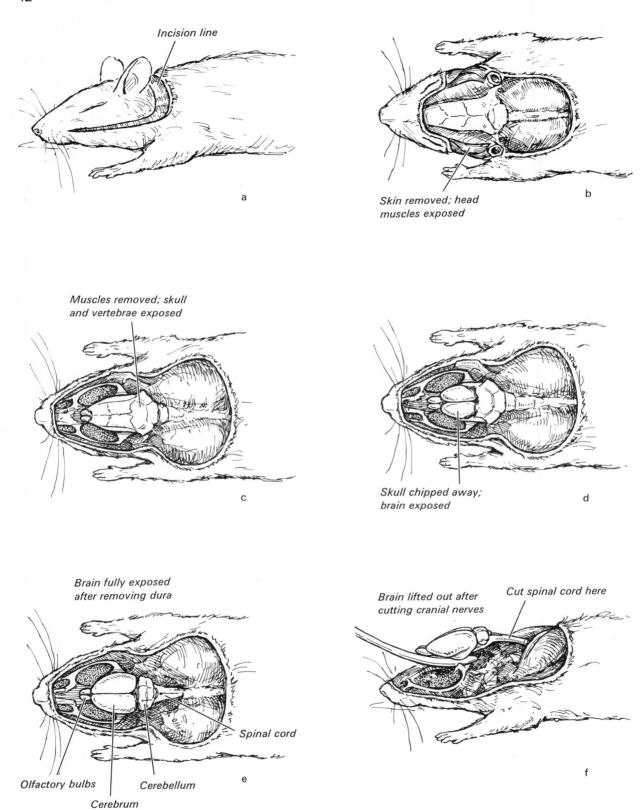

FIGURE 2-13. *Exposing and removing the brain from a perfused rat.*

REFERENCES

Hoebel, B. G., 1964. Electrode-Cannulas for electrical or chemical treatment of multiple brain sites. *Electroenceph. Clin. Neurophysiol.* **16**, 399–402.

Miller, N. E., E. E. Coons, M. Lewis, and O. D. Jensen, 1961. Electrode holders in chronic preparations. A simple technique for use with the rat. In D. E. Sheer (Ed.), *Electrical stimulation of the brain*, pp. 51–54. Austin, University of Texas Press.

Rowland, V., 1966. Stereotaxic techniques and the production of lesions. In L. Martini and W. F. Ganong (Eds.), *Neuroendocrinology*, Vol. 1, pp. 107–132. New York, Academic Press.

Valenstein, E. S., W. Hodos, and L. A. Stein, 1961. A simplified electrode-assembly for implanting chronic electrodes in the brains of small animals. *Amer. J. Psychol.* **74**, 125–128

SOURCES OF MATERIALS

Sources are not mentioned for common laboratory materials or glassware. These items, if not already on hand, are readily available from several general laboratory or hospital supply houses. Items that instructors may have some difficulty finding are listed under either the category of materials needed by individual groups (2-4 students) or the category of materials that may be shared by two or more groups. Usually no more than four groups, and preferably fewer, should share a piece of equipment. When several sources are listed it would be best to obtain catalogs or brochures for all of them and choose the most suitable. The lists of sources are not, of course, necessarily complete.

MATERIALS NEEDED BY INDIVIDUAL GROUPS

Rat skulls ($4–$5 each)
  SOURCE: Turtox
Rat-restraining device ($10–$15 each)
  SOURCE: Clay-Adams
Insect pins ($1–$2 per 100)
  SOURCES: Clay-Adams, Carolina, Turtox, Wards
Epoxylite varnish ($5–$6 per pint)
  SOURCE: Epoxylite
Acrylic dental cement ($5–$10 per kit)
  SOURCES: Acralite, Caulk
Surgical instruments: in addition to the instruments used for dissection in Section 1, each team will need a needle holder, bone-cutting forceps or rongeurs, at least 2 curved mosquito hemostatic forceps, and several 1-inch or 2-inch curved cutting-edge suture needles ($25–$40 per team)
  SOURCES: American Hospital, Carolina, Clay-Adams, Turtox, Wards, Aloe

MATERIALS THAT CAN BE SHARED BY TWO OR MORE GROUPS

Stereotaxic instrument ($150–$500 each)
  SOURCES: Davis Kopf, Lab-Tronics, Lehigh Valley, Scientific Prototype, Stoelting

Lesion maker ($100–$200 each)
  SOURCES: Lehigh Valley, Steolting
Stimulator ($80–$200)
  SOURCES: Lehigh Valley, Stoelting
Surgical instruments: 2-cc hypodermic syringes $2–$3 each) and 22-gauge $\frac{1}{2}$-inch needles ($2–$3 per dozen), 00 silk suture material ($2–$3 for 25 yards)
  SOURCES: Aloe, American Hospital
Electrical supplies: miniature alligator clips (10c–20c each), copper wire ($1–$2 per $\frac{1}{2}$-pound spool, solder ($1–$2 per 1-pound spool)
  SOURCES: Lafayette, Allied
Animal balance ($20–$50)
  SOURCES: Carolina, Turtox, Wards, Scientific Products, Arthur H. Thomas, Van Waters and Rogers
Perfusion apparatus: 3-way stop cork ($6–$10 each), plastic jugs ($10–$20 each)
  SOURCES: Scientific Products, Arthur H. Thomas, Van Waters and Rogers
Electric Drill: Dremel Moto Tool for drilling holes in skull ($30–$35 each)
  SOURCES: Lafayette, Allied
Drugs: sodium pentobarbital, atropine sulfate solution, penicillin-streptomycin combination antibiotic
  SOURCES: See *Physicians' Desk Reference to Pharmaceutical Specialties and Biologicals* for manufacturers and trade names (published annually by Medical Economics, Inc. Oradell, New Jersey).

COMMERCIAL ADDRESSES

Acralite Company, Inc.
  6095 12th Street
  Detroit, Michigan 48208
Allied Electronics
  100 N. Western Avenue
  Chicago, Illinois 60680
Aloe Medical
  1831 Olive Street
  St. Louis, Missouri 63103

American Hospital Supplies
  2020 Ridge Avenue
  Evanston, Illinois 60201
Carolina Biological Supply Company
  Burlington, North Carolina 27216
L. D. Caulk Company
  P.O. Box 359
  Millford, Delaware 19963
Clay-Adams, Inc.
  141 E. 25th Street
  New York, New York 10010
Epoxylite Corporation
  1428 N. Tyler Avenue
  P.O. Box 3397
  South El Monte, California
Davis Kopf Instruments
  7324 Elmo Street
  Tujunga, California 91042
Lab-Tronics
  H. Neuman and Company
  8136 North Lawndale Avenue
  Skokie, Illinois 60076
Lafayette Radio Electronics
  111 Jericho Turnpike
  Syosset, Long Island, New York 11791
Lehigh Valley Electronics

Box 125
Fogelsville, Pennsylvania 18051
Scientific Prototype Manufacturing Corporation
  615 W. 131 Street
  New York, New York 10027
C. H. Stoelting Company
  424 N. Homan Avenue
  Chicago, Illinois 60624
Arthur H. Thomas Company
  Vine Street at Third
  P.O. Box 779
  Philadelphia, Pennsylvania 18105
Turtox Products
  General Biological Supply House
  8200 South Hoyne Avenue
  Chicago, Illinois 60620
Van Waters and Rogers
  P.O. Box 3200
  Rincon Annex
  San Francisco, California 94119
Ward's Natural Science
  P.O. Box 1712
  Rochester, New York 14603
Ward's of California
  P.O. Box 1749
  Monterey, California 93942

EXPERIMENTS IN NEUROPSYCHOLOGY

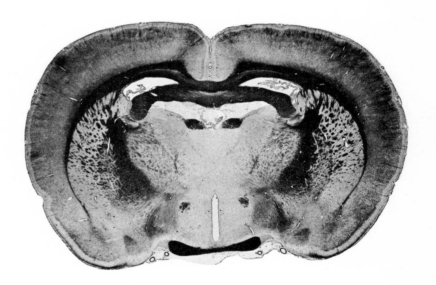

INTRODUCTION

The four experiments in this section are examples of many possibilities for neuropsychological experiments. Your instructor may have you conduct different experiments, or he may have you conduct some of these plus others of his own design and choosing. These particular experiments are based upon research investigations that have been reported in various professional journals and that have been successfully replicated by students. Bear in mind, however, that you, as a student investigator, are attempting to replicate the experimental findings of others; results are not guaranteed even if directions are followed closely. The experiments were chosen to illustrate experimental methods in neuropsychology with which you should be familiar; namely, lesioning parts of the brain, implanting electrodes, and examining the brain to determine the area lesioned or stimulated.

It is assumed that you are familiar with the structure of the mammalian brain from your study of Section 1. You should also be familiar with the various experimental techniques and principles outlined in Section 2 and have practiced all the techniques used in lesioning and electrode implantation on dead rats. You will need to consult the stereotaxic atlas (Section 4) as you perform each experiment.

The four experiments will take about five laboratory periods (of 3 or 4 hours) for a team of two to four students to conduct. Several laboratory periods will be needed to conduct each experiment, because intervals of a few days are needed for animals to recover from surgery, for behavioral effects to take place in the course of time, or for the brain to fix in formalin before being sectioned and stained. Since parts of several experiments should be conducted simultaneously, each experiment should be planned well in advance. Some experiments will require more laboratory periods than others. They are arranged in order of decreasing amount of time required. Sectioning, staining, and examination of the brain for all experiments can be done in the final (fifth) laboratory period. It is important that you read through an entire experiment before beginning work.

Your instructor may give you a schedule of procedures to be accomplished each period. It is suggested that one student from each team be selected to take responsibility for seeing that the work for a particular experiment be completed each week, and for reporting the experiment for the team.

When preparing a report of an experiment, the student responsible for the experiment should consult with individuals in other teams responsible for the same experiment so that he can discuss the results of the entire class in his report. If possible, the laboratory reports should contain some statistical verification. Part E of this section includes an explanation of the use of nonparametric statistics for neuropsychological experiments and tables that are quite useful for small groups of subjects. At the end of the section are unlabeled brain section drawings that can be used to illustrate the extent of lesions or location of electrode placements that were used in the experiments.

Changes in Feeding Behavior Following Ventromedial Hypothalamic Lesions

Studies during the last few decades have led to the concept that the hypothalamus contains regions or "centers" that control feeding behavior. Electrical stimulation of the ventrolateral hypothalamic region induces feeding or eating, whereas stimulation of the ventromedial hypothalamic region suppresses feeding. Ablation of ventrolateral region supposedly produces aphagia, or lack of eating, and ablation of the ventromedial region often causes hyperphagia, or overeating. It is easiest to interpret changes that lead to overeating since this behavior represents an increase in behavioral activity, whereas aphagia might be merely the general debilitating effect of a lesion. Because destruction of the ventromedial nucleus causes overeating behavior, it is possible to determine the effect of such a lesion by monitoring the difference in weight gain between lesioned animals and control animals.

Each team should use at least one experimental animal and one control animal. Procedures will be the same for both, except that current will not be passed through the electrodes in control animals.

PROCEDURE

Laboratory Period 1

Carefully weigh each rat and record weights for further reference. The rat should then be anesthetized. While waiting for the animal to become sufficiently anesthetized, clip the hair on its head and review the coordinates for the bilateral lesions in the ventromedial hypothalamic nucleus. At this point, your instructor should explain the use of the lesion maker you will be using. After the animal has become fully anesthetized place the head in the stereotaxic frame. Make an incision to expose the skull. After computing stereotaxic adjustments, determine where the holes should be made and drill them for bilateral electrode placement. Make a lesion by passing a current of .2 ma for 15 seconds. Close the skin with simple interrupted sutures, and inject antibiotic into the thigh muscle. Repeat the above procedure on the control rats but do not pass any current through the electrodes. When you return the rats to their cages, be sure the cages are labeled so that each rat may be identified.

For 2 to 3 days after surgery the rats will lose weight merely as a result of surgery. Usually, the lesioned animal will lose the most weight. A comparison of differential weight gain can only be made after the animals have started to gain weight. The differential weight gain is generally the greatest when animals are fed (ad lib) a very palatable food such as meat meal for several weeks.

Laboratory Periods 2 through 4

Record the weights of both experimental and control rats every second or third day for 20 to 30 days. The longer the period of observation, the better are the chances of obtaining differential weight gain measures and seeing the experimental rat become obese.

After making the final weight recording, perfuse the brain with saline and 10% formalin while the animal is deeply anesthetized. Remove the brain and store in 10% formalin for at least 3 or 4 days before sectioning for examination of the lesions.

Laboratory Period 5

Section and stain the lesioned brain according to instructions in Section 1C or your instructor's directions. Refer to a stereotaxic atlas to determine the approximate location and extent of the lesions. Outline the extent of the lesions on the brain section illustrations provided at the end of this section.

RESULTS

On graph paper, plot mean body weight versus time (in days or weeks) for all experimental rats in which the ventromedial nucleus was actually lesioned. Plot a separate graph for nonlesioned controls. If there are sufficient data, use nonparametric statistical tests to determine if there is a significant (e.g., $p < .05$) difference in weight gain between the experimentals and the controls. Briefly discuss the data and the implications of the results concerning the effect of the hypothalamus on eating or feeding behavior.

Changes in Mating Behavior in Male Rats with Brain Lesions

The control of mating behavior, like the control of other stereotyped forms of behavior such as feeding or fighting, is believed to be largely mediated by subcortical neural structures. Such structures or areas supposedly integrate excitatory and inhibitory neural influences resulting from sensory stimuli (visual, olfactory, auditory) from members of the opposite sex, stimulation of genital sensory receptors, and the action of gonadal hormones on the brain. It follows that stimulation or ablation of these structures may markedly alter mating behavior. Electrical stimulation of parts of the hypothalamus has been shown to evoke mating behavior in male rats. In other experiments, lesions in the posterior part of the diencephalon or in the anterior mesencephalon have caused an increase in male sexual activity. A region of the brain that seems to be particularly important as a neural integration region for mating behavior is the medial preoptic area. It is in this region that implantation of testosterone may evoke mating activity in castrated sexually inactive male rats and it is only in this region that small lesions may abolish mating behavior in sexually active males.

In this experiment you will attempt to abolish mating activity in the male rat by lesioning the medial preoptic nucleus. Important in the interpretation of this effect will be the consideration that the reduction in mating activity is not due to general debilitation. Thus, it will be important to monitor and compare changes in weight and in general activity (in an open field activity box). Control subjects should be treated in the same manner except that current will not be passed through the electrode. In the experiment, how-ever, some of the lesioned subjects will probably continue to mate, and these you can use as controls, monitoring changes in body weight and general activity and comparing them with animals in which mating activity has been abolished or markedly reduced. Each team of students should use at least two animals.

As an alternative to lesioning the medial preoptic nucleus, your instructor may want you to lesion the diencephalic-mesencephalic junction in an attempt to increase mating activity or to implant testosterone propionate into the medial preoptic nucleus in order to restore mating activity in castrates (details for this procedure are given in some of the references listed for this section).

PROCEDURE

Laboratory Period 1

PREOPERATIVE GENERAL ACTIVITY TEST

Each team of students should test two sexually active male rats that have been previously screened for sexual activity. Place each experimental rat in an open field activity box (similar to the one used in Part C) in a quiet, dimly lit room, and count the number of squares each subject enters in the course of a 5-minute period (see Part C for details).

Clear plastic front

FIGURE 3-1. *Mating behavior in an observation box.*

FIRST PREOPERATIVE MATING TEST

Tests for mating behavior of the rats should be conducted in a dimly illuminated, quiet room; use a box with a clear plastic front, such as the one shown in Figure 3-1, or a cardboard box (with the lid off) at least 16 in. x 16 in. Make the adult female rats behaviorally receptive by the administration of .1 mg of estradiol benzoate 48 to 72 hours before testing, and 1 mg of progesterone 5 hours before testing. Because this procedure does not make all females receptive, three or four females should be injected for every two males to be tested. A male should be placed alone in the mating box for about five minutes so that he will become accustomed to the environment. Then the female should be placed in the box, and observations of mating activity should be made for the next 30 minutes. If she is receptive, the female will allow the male to mount her and will exhibit lordosis (backward arching of the back) during the male's mounting. The sexually active male rat will mount and rapidly penetrate the female (intromission) several times at intervals of about 10 to 60 seconds. After each penetration, which takes about $\frac{1}{3}$ of a second, the male "throws himself" backwards off the female. After approximately 5 to 15 penetrations, or intromissions, the male will penetrate the female, but instead of throwing himself backwards, he will appear to rest

upon the female. This represents an ejaculatory response. The male will remain sexually inactive for approximately five to seven minutes after an ejaculation. Record the number of penetrations or intromissions and the number of ejaculations the male exhibits in a 30-minute period.

Laboratory Period 2

SECOND PREOPERATIVE MATING TEST

Conduct a second mating test on each male rat, using the same procedure as in the initial mating test. It is best not to run two tests for general activity because the subject may adapt to the open field activity box. Surgery for placement of the lesions can be performed immediately after the second mating test.

SURGERY

Carefully weigh each rat and record weights for further reference. Anesthetize the rat with sodium pentobarbital. While waiting for the animal to become sufficiently anesthetized, clip the hair on its head and review the coordinates for placing bilateral lesions in the middle of the medial preoptic nucleus. Also, have your instructor explain the use of the lesion maker you will be using. After the animal has become sufficiently anesthetized for surgery, place the head in the stereotaxic frame. Make an incision to expose the skull. After computing stereotaxic adjustments, determine where the holes should be made, and drill them for bilateral electrode placement. Make a lesion by passing a direct current of 2 ma for 15 seconds. Close the skin with simple interrupted sutures, and inject antibiotic into the thigh muscles.

Laboratory Period 3

FIRST POSTOPERATIVE MATING TEST

Conduct a mating test on each lesioned subject about 7 days after the surgery. However, first make sure the female is receptive by placing a known sexually active male in the testing chamber and observing the female's reactions. If both lesioned subjects are inactive for 30 minutes, try a different receptive female for a few minutes. If a lesioned subject does not ejaculate it will be necessary to conduct another mating test in another 7 days.

Laboratory Period 4

FINAL PREOPERATIVE TESTS

Conduct a test for general activity. A second mating test should be conducted for those subjects that did

not ejaculate on the first postoperative test. Also record the weight of the animal.

REMOVAL OF THE BRAIN

Perfuse the brain with saline and 10% formalin while the animal is deeply anesthetized. Remove the brain and store in 10% formalin for at least 3 to 4 days before sectioning for examination of the lesion.

Laboratory Period 5

Section and stain the brain of the lesioned subjects according to instructions in Section 1C, or your instructor's directions. Determine the location and extent of the lesions with the use of a stereotaxic atlas. Outline the extent of the lesions on the brain section illustrations provided at the end of this section.

RESULTS

Tabulate data for all experimental animals tested in the class. For the mating tests, tabulate the number of intromissions and ejaculations per 30-minute test for the two preoperative and postoperative tests. Also tabulate preoperative and postoperative weight and general activity scores. Compare the location of lesions, mating activity, body weight, and general activity of the lesioned animals that showed no apparent reduction in mating activity with those of the animals in which mating activity was markedly reduced or abolished. Briefly discuss possible interpretation of the results.

Changes in General Activity
Following Lesions of the Hippocampus

Some studies showing an increase in general activity after lesions of the hippocampus suggest that the hippocampus is, in some way, related to the control of general activity. The purpose of the following experiment will be to test this finding. One of the methodological problems confronting one in studies involving brain lesions is that the cessation of a particular behavior may be due to the general debilitating effect of the lesion. But when there is an increase in some aspect of behavior, the results may be inter-preted without reference to the possibility of general debilitation. The proposed outcome of this experiment demonstrates this principle.

The general activity in rats can be measured by several techniques. One of the simplest is to use some quantitative procedure to determine how much a rat runs around in an open space or field. This may be done by placing a rat in the middle of a large box, 3 or 4 feet square, that has been divided into squares. The chief methodological problem here is that the rat's in-

FIGURE 3-2. *A box with the floor marked off into equal sized squares so that general activity may be quantified.*

creasing familiarity with the testing apparatus may be a factor in the postoperative data, so that an increase or decrease in general activity might be interpreted as a function of familiarity rather than as a result of the lesion. Therefore, a group of animals will be needed for controls.

Each team of students should work with at least two rats. These should be male animals, since general activity of females tends to change with the estrous cycle. The hippocampus will be bilaterally lesioned in one animal. The control animal will undergo the same surgery, except that no current will be passed through the electrode.

PROCEDURE

Laboratory Period 1

PREOPERATIVE TESTING

An animal's general activity can be measured by recording the number of squares in the activity box it enters in a given period of time. You should decide upon a criterion for determining whether the rat has entered a square. For example, you may arbitrarily decide that a rat enters a square when the ears or the shoulders cross a line. Use the same criterion in all tests. You may also wish to count the number of times the animal stands up on the sides of the box. It is important to make observations in a quiet room or in a part of the room in which there are a minimum of distractions. Place the activity box on the floor but stand as far from the box as possible while observing so that you are not seen by the rat. Count the number of squares entered in a 5- or 10-minute period. If possible, two people should do the counting and the results averaged (if there are differences). Also make qualitative observations of behavior, noting, for example, whether the animal stays near the sides, stops frequently, or keeps moving in circles.

SURGERY

Anesthetize the rat with sodium pentobarbital. While waiting for the animal to become sufficiently anesthetized, clip the hair on its head and review the stereotaxic coordinates to be used for bilateral lesion of the middle of the dorsal hippocampus. At this point, your instructor should explain the use of the lesion

maker you will be using. After the animal has been anesthetized for surgery, place the head in the stereotaxic frame. Make an incision to expose the skull. After computing stereotaxic adjustments mark where holes should be made and drill them for bilateral electrode placement. Lower the electrode to each placement and make a lesion by passing a current of 2 ma for 1 minute. Close the skin with simple interrupted sutures, and inject antibiotic into the muscle of the thigh.

Repeat the above procedures on your control rat but do not pass any current through the electrodes. When the animals are returned to their cages, be sure the cages are labeled so that each rat may be identified.

Rats usually recover within 2–3 days after surgery. However, it is desirable to wait about a week after surgery before running postoperative tests.

Laboratory Period 2

POSTOPERATIVE TESTING

Retest the control and experimental animals for general activity in the same manner as in the preoperative test. Take caution that the amount of light and the number of distractions are about the same as in the preoperative testing. Another set of postoperative tests may be conducted in another week if you so desire. If there is too much postoperative testing, however, adaptation to the activity box may result.

REMOVAL OF THE BRAIN

Perfuse the brain with saline and 10% formalin while the animal is deeply anesthetized. Remove the brain and store in 10% formalin for at least 3 or 4 days before sectioning for examination and location of the lesion.

Laboratory Period 3

Section and stain the brain of the lesioned animal according to instructions in Section 1C or your instructor's directions. Determine the location and extent of the lesion with the use of a stereotaxic atlas. Outline the extent of the lesions on the brain section illustrations provided at the end of this section.

RESULTS

Tabulate the data for animals from the entire class, showing preoperative and postoperative general activity scores for rats subjected to bilateral hippocampal lesions and control operations. Include in your report your outline of the brain lesions. Determine whether there are enough animals to use a statistical test. If so apply the appropriate nonparametric test and give the significance of the results. Briefly state possible interpretations of the function of the hippocampus in general activity.

Reinforcement of Behavior
with Intracranial Electrical Stimulation

Several areas of the brain, when electrically stimulated in the conscious animal (by chronically implanted electrodes), are very reinforcing, or rewarding, to the animal. These areas are loosely labeled "pleasure centers" but are more accurately referred to as self-stimulation areas. The term self-stimulation is applied because one way to determine whether an electrode is in such a region is to give the animal an opportunity to stimulate, or to control the stimula-

tion of, its own brain. This can be done by making it possible for the animal to learn to press a lever that closes a switch delivering a train of electrical pulses to its brain.

In this experiment electrical brain stimulation (EBS) will be used as a primary reinforcer, such as food or water, to shape a behavioral response, in much the same way that food and water can be used to shape behavioral responses. Two structures that,

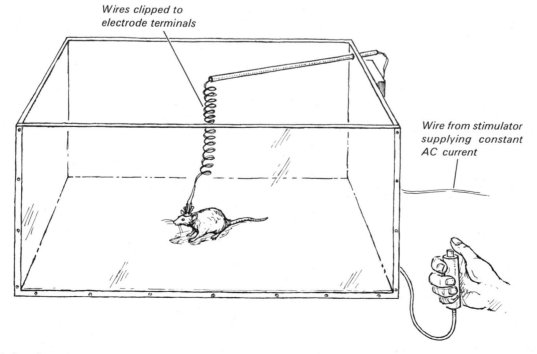

Wires clipped to electrode terminals

Wire from stimulator supplying constant AC current

FIGURE 3-3. *A rat about to receive electrical stimulation.*

when stimulated, frequently yield behaviorally reinforcing effects are the septal nuclei and the medial forebrain bundle. This medial forebrain bundle is made up of a series of short nerve fibers interconnecting the septal area, the preoptic region, the hypothalamus (particularly the lateral hypothalamus) and the midbrain. It is easiest to contact the greatest number of fibers of this bundle in the lateral hypothalamus.

Each team of students should implant electrodes in at least two animals. You may implant either one electrode or two in each animal, depending upon your skill in implanting electrodes.

PROCEDURE

Laboratory Period 1

SURGERY

No preoperative testing is necessary. Anesthetize the rat with sodium pentobarbital. While waiting for the animal to become sufficiently anesthetized, clip the hair on its head and review the stereotaxic coordinates to be used to implant an electrode in the septal area of one animal and in the lateral hypothalamus in another. After the animal has become sufficiently anesthetized for surgery, place the head in the stereotaxic frame. Make an incision to expose the skull. After computing stereotaxic adjustments, determine where holes should be made and drill them for the electrode implant. Unless your instructor designates a particular type of electrode or pedestal for this experiment, follow the directions given in Section 2D for implanting electrodes and building the plastic pedestal. Just before the skin is sutured around the pedestal sprinkle antibacterial powder into the wound. Inject antibiotic into the muscle of the animal's thigh. The animal will require 2 to 3 days to recover from surgery.

Laboratory Period 2

BEHAVIORAL TESTING

Your instructor will explain how to operate the particular stimulator you will be using. He may suggest specific electrical parameters; if he does not, use a .5-second pulse train of current alternating at about 50 or 60 cycles per second. A hand switch may be used to deliver the .5-second pulse train. Place the animal in a testing box and attach leads from the stimulator. Set the voltage at less than 1 volt, attach leads to the rat, and slowly raise the voltage, trying out each level as you proceed. Watch for a light twitch of the head when the animal is stimulated. If the stimulus is rewarding the animal may appear to look around to see from where it is coming. If the stimulus appears to be aversive, lower the current.

Place the animal in a box that contains one or two levers, and try to shape a certain response, such as pressing a lever or going to a corner (Figure 3-3). This is done by reinforcing (with two or three pulses) any movement in the direction of the desired response. Deliver the stimulus as soon as the rat makes an appropriate movement. Continue reinforcing appropriate behavior, but slowly raise your criterion (that is, withhold reinforcement until the animal is closer to making the desired response) until the rat presses a lever, goes directly to a corner, or makes whatever other response that you are trying to evoke.

If you are not familiar with the procedures for shaping behavior, it would be advisable to read Skinner's article on teaching animals (see references). You might also try the following exercise with members of your team: one member of the group (as the subject) should go to the other side of the room while the others (the experimenters) decide on some simple behavioral act such as touching a light switch, picking up a book, or turning on a water faucet. Have the subject return but give him or her no verbal information regarding the behavioral act. The subject should know that when he is approaching the "correct" object he will hear the click of a cricket or similar noise maker. Hearing a click, or, in essence, being "correct," is reinforcing for humans. The subject then should wander around attempting to obtain reinforcement. The experimenters should proceed to shape the subject's behavior by withholding reinforcement until the subject moves in the direction of the correct object. Next raise the criterion of reinforcement so that the subject receives no reinforcement until he is quite close to the correct object. Raise the criterion again, withholding reinforcement until the subject makes the correct response. It is important that the click be given within a fraction of a second after the correct response at any given criterion.

LESIONING AND REMOVING THE BRAIN

After thoroughly testing each implanted animal, it is necessary, in order to determine the location of the electrode, to pass a current strong enough to cause a lesion at the tip of each electrode. To do this inject a dose of anesthetic about three times the amount needed to anesthetize an animal. With a lesion maker, pass a .5-ma current for 30 seconds. Immediately perfuse and remove the brain.

Laboratory Period 3

Section and stain the brain according to instructions in Section 1C or your instructor's directions. Deter-mine the location of the electrodes for both nonrein-forcing and reinforcing placements. Mark with an "X" the approximate location of the electrode on the brain section illustrations provided at the end of this section.

RESULTS

Prepare a report of the results, showing in which of the placements EBS was reinforcing. Discuss the criteria that were employed to distinguish reinforcing from nonreinforcing areas.

Reporting Experimental Results

NONPARAMETRIC STATISTICAL ANALYSIS OF DATA

In your report of experimental results you will want to illustrate the results of altering brain function. The drawings of brain sections provided here are actually small scale unlabeled replicas of the brain sections in the stereotaxic atlas (Section 4) and may be used to outline the extent of brain lesions or the location of stimulating electrodes.

If possible, you will also want to verify any interpretations of your data by using statistical procedures such as those outlined below.

In interpreting data from most behavioral and physiological experiments, one is interested in determining, by statistical procedures, whether the differences obtained from various treatments are real differences or merely the reflection of chance variation. You will have to determine this when you are interpreting data that has been submitted by the entire class for a group of subjects. It is assumed that you are familiar with statistical measures of central tendency (mean, median, and mode) and measures of dispersion (such as range and standard deviation) as well as some parametric statistical procedures commonly used to determine whether two groups of scores are significantly different. If you think you need a general review of the use of statistical tests, you may wish to consult the book by Siegel (see references) or one of the several available texts on statistics and experimental psychology.

The term "parametric" refers to population values, which are called parameters and to which inferences are made on the basis of small samples. Parametric procedures are based on the assumption that the sample scores are drawn from populations in which characteristics or behavioral traits are normally distributed. Parametric procedures also assume that sample scores are truly numerical and not merely rank orders. In many neuropsychological studies the experimenter may be studying behavioral phenomena about which no assumptions of a distribution within a population can be made. Also, in many experiments, the method of measuring behavioral changes cannot be assumed to result in truly numerical scores but only in rank orders of intensity or magnitude. Several nonparametric statistical procedures that are ideally suited to data analysis in neuropsychology have been developed. In these tests it is not necessary that scores under analysis be drawn from a population that has a certain distribution, or that the scores be truly numerical. The fact that some of the tests have been adapted for use with small samples makes them particularly useful since complex and time-consuming procedures in neuropsychology frequently limit an investigator to a small number of subjects. In addition, nonparametric procedures require a minimal amount of mathematical computation, so that the investigator can be freed from excessive concern with the suitability of an experimental design for certain statistical procedures. He can, instead, concentrate on using relevant control procedures and precise methods, and on collecting meaningful data.

The chief disadvantage of nonparametric methods is that they do not have the statistical power of parametric procedures if they are applied to data that come from a population of values that are actually normally distributed. Essentially what this means is

Subject	Preoperative score	Postoperative score	Difference between preoperative and postoperative scores	Rank of absolute difference	Smaller sum of like-signed ranks
A	14	24	10	8	
B	22	30	8	6	
C	19	18	−1	1.5	1.5
D	21	21	0	—	
E	13	15	2	3	
F	15	20	5	4	
G	21	32	9	7	
H	17	23	6	5	
I	26	25	−1	1.5	1.5
				$N = 8$	$T = 3$

that—if one is working with small numbers of animals—the differences between groups of subjects must be very reliable and quite large to achieve a significance at some given level of probability. This is usually no problem, however, since most neuropsychological work is meaningful only if there is a very marked and reliable alteration of behavior. Two nonparametric tests are discussed in this part. These and many other nonparametric tests have been organized into a very useful reference source by Siegel.

Most experiments in neuropsychology consist of altering brain function and observing the results. Depending upon the particular problem and the methods, either of two experimental designs is most commonly employed: (1) The animal is used as his own control and preoperative and postoperative behavioral responses are compared; (2) a control group is used along with an experimental group of subjects, and the postoperative scores are compared or the differences between preoperative and postoperative scores for the two groups are compared. In the first experimental design, scores are from related samples (the same animal) and the Wilcoxon match-pairs signed-ranks test may be used. In the second experimental design, scores are from independent samples (different animals) and the Mann-Whitney test may be used. Tables of significance of these two tests are given for two-tailed and one-tailed analysis.* If the direction of the outcome of the experiment is definitely predicted before, the one-tailed tables may be

used. In most neuropsychological work, however, it is best to use the two-tailed table to determine significance. Your instructor may indicate when it is appropriate for you to use one-tailed tests.

WILCOXON MATCHED-PAIRS SIGNED-RANKS TEST

This test may be employed when the animal is to be his own control. Preoperative and postoperative pairs of scores are compared for each subject. The N (number of subjects) for this test is the total number of animals in which preoperative and postoperative scores are compared. The preoperative and postoperative scores may be single measurements or means of several measurements. This test gives more weight to a pair of scores that shows a large difference than to a pair that shows a small difference.

The preoperative and postoperative scores (whether they be single measurements or means of several measurements) are matched for each subject. The differences between preoperative and postoperative scores for each animal are calculated, and are then arranged, regardless of arithmetical sign ($\pm$), in order of increasing magnitude. The smallest (absolute) difference is given a rank of one and all subsequent differences are given respectively greater ranks. If the difference between the preoperative and postoperative score should be zero, the difference is not considered in the rank order and that subject is not included in the total N. If two or more differences are of the same size, the tied cases are given the same rank, the rank being the average of ranks that would have been assigned if the difference scores were not the same but had differed slightly. The difference score that immediately follows the tied scores is then given the

---

*In a one-tailed test you are predicting that the experimental groups will differ in only one direction from the control group. In a two-tailed test you are determining whether the experimental group differs in either a greater or lesser magnitude from the control group.

same rank it would have been given if all scores preceding it had differed slightly. After scores for all subjects are ranked, the arithmetical signs of the differences between preoperative and postoperative scores are then assigned to each of the ranks. The smaller sum of like-signed ranks is added to obtain T. Thus T is either the sum of positive ranks or the sum of negative ranks. In referring to the tables of T values, the T that you obtain from experimental data must be equal or less than the T given in the tables for any given N in order for you to obtain the level of significance indicated at the top of the column.

The table on page 59 is an example of the calculation of T for a hypothetical experimental result.

In referring to Table 3-1, the two-tailed table, for the Wilcoxon test it can be seen that a T of 4 or less for an N of 8 is significant at the $p < .05$ level. The experimental result is not significant at the $p < .01$ level.

Tables 3-1 and 3-2 give T values and their associated levels of significance for an N of subjects from 5 through 20.

MANN-WHITNEY U TEST

This test is used when the control and experimental subjects are separate animals. The number of subjects for each group may differ.

A score or mean of scores for each subject, which may represent postoperative scores or differences between preoperative and postoperative scores for each subject, are listed in order of increasing magnitude (the algebraic or actual sign is considered). If the mean of scores from the experimental group exceeds the mean of scores from the control group, then for each control score determine the number of experimental scores that precede it in magnitude. The sum of the number of times an experimental score precedes a control score is determined to obtain U. In referring to tables of U values the U that you obtain from your experimental data must be equal or less than the U given in the tables for any given set of N's in order for you to obtain the level of significance indicated at the top of the column.

Note that no experimental scores precede the control scores of W and Y. The control score of X is preceded by two experimental scores (those of subjects A and E), and the control score of Z is preceded by one experimental score (that of subject A).

In referring to the two-tailed table of U values for the Mann-Whitney test, you can see that a U of 3 for Ns of 6 and 4 is not significant at the $p < .05$ level.

If the mean of scores from the experimental group is smaller than the mean of scores from the control

group, then for each experimental score determine the number of control scores that precede it in magnitude and add these to obtain U. If ties occur between two or more scores involving both groups then take a conservative approach and consider that there is a slight difference between the tied subjects, causing U to be larger.

The following is an example of a calculation of U for a hypothetical experimental result.

Results from Experimental Subjects

Subject	Preoperative score	Postoperative score	Difference
A	7	12	5
B	25	40	15
C	17	29	12
D	28	42	14
E	21	28	7
F	3	12	9

Results from Control Subjects

Subject	Preoperative score	Postoperative score	Difference
W	8	10	2
X	12	20	8
Y	10	9	−1
Z	24	30	6

Determination of U

Control Subject	Number of experimental scores (difference) preceding each control score
W	0
X	2
Y	0
Z	1
	$U = 3$

Tables 3-3 and 3-4 give U values and their associated levels of significance for groups consisting of 2 to 15 subjects.

TABLE 3-1 Table of *T* Values for Two-tailed Wilcoxon Matched-pairs Signed-Ranks Test

	Level of Significance	
N	$p<.05$	$p<.01$
5	—	—
6	0	—
7	2	—
8	3	0
9	5	1
10	8	3
11	10	5
12	13	7
13	17	9
14	21	12
15	25	15
16	29	19
17	34	23
18	40	27
19	46	32
20	52	37

TABLE 3-2 Table of *T* Values for One-tailed Wilcoxon Matched-pairs Signed-Ranks Test

	Level of Significance	
N	$p<.05$	$p<.01$
5	0	—
6	2	—
7	3	0
8	5	1
9	8	3
10	10	5
11	13	7
12	17	9
13	21	12
14	25	15
15	30	19
16	35	23
17	41	27
18	47	32
19	53	37
20	60	43

TABLE 3-3 Table of U Values for Two-tailed Mann-Whitney Test

N Smaller	N Larger													
	3		4		5		6		7		8		9	
	$p<.05$	$p<.01$	$p<.05$	$p<.01$	$p<.05$	$p<.01$	$p<.05$	$p<.01$	$p<.05$	$p<.01$	$p<.05$	$p<.01$	$p<.05$	$p<.01$
2	—	—	—	—	—	—	—	—	—	—	0	—	0	—
3	—	—	—	—	0	—	1	—	1	—	2	—	2	0
4			0	—	1	—	2	0	3	0	4	1	4	1
5					2	0	3	1	5	1	6	2	7	3
6							5	2	6	3	8	4	10	5
7									8	4	10	6	12	7
8											13	7	15	9
9													17	11
10														
11														
12														
13														
14														
15														

N Smaller	N Larger											
	10		11		12		13		14		15	
	$p<.05$	$p<.01$	$p<.05$	$p<.01$	$p<.05$	$p<.01$	$p<.05$	$p<.01$	$p<.05$	$p<.01$	$p<.05$	$p<.01$
2	0	—	0	—	1	—	1	—	1	—	1	—
3	3	0	3	0	4	1	4	1	5	1	5	2
4	5	2	6	2	7	3	8	3	9	4	10	5
5	8	4	9	5	11	6	12	7	13	7	14	8
6	11	6	13	7	14	9	16	10	17	11	19	12
7	14	9	16	10	18	12	20	13	22	15	24	16
8	17	11	19	13	22	15	24	17	26	18	29	20
9	20	13	23	16	26	18	28	20	31	22	34	24
10	23	16	26	18	29	21	33	24	36	26	39	29
11			30	21	33	24	37	27	40	30	44	33
12					37	27	41	31	45	34	49	37
13							45	34	50	38	54	42
14									55	42	59	46
15											64	51

TABLE 3-4 Table of *U* Values for One-tailed Mann-Whitney Test

N Smaller	*N* Larger													
	3		4		5		6		7		8		9	
	$p<.05$	$p<.01$	$p<.05$	$p<.01$	$p<.05$	$p<.01$	$p<.05$	$p<.01$	$p<.05$	$p<.01$	$p<.05$	$p<.01$	$p<.05$	$p<.01$
2	—	—	—	—	0	—	0	—	0	—	1	—	1	—
3	0	—	0	—	1	—	2	—	2	0	3	0	3	1
4			1	—	2	0	3	1	4	1	5	2	6	3
5					4	1	5	2	6	3	8	4	9	5
6							7	3	8	4	10	6	12	7
7									11	6	13	7	15	9
8											15	9	18	11
9													21	14
10														
11														
12														
13														
14														
15														

N Smaller	*N* Larger											
	10		11		12		13		14		15	
	$p<.05$	$p<.01$	$p<.05$	$p<.01$	$p<.05$	$p<.01$	$p<.05$	$p<.01$	$p<.05$	$p<.01$	$p<.05$	$p<.01$
2	1	—	1	—	2	—	2	0	2	0	3	0
3	4	1	5	1	5	2	6	2	7	2	7	3
4	7	3	8	4	9	5	10	5	11	6	12	7
5	11	6	12	7	13	8	15	9	16	10	18	11
6	14	8	16	9	17	11	19	12	21	13	23	15
7	17	11	19	12	21	14	24	16	26	17	28	19
8	20	13	23	15	26	17	28	20	31	22	33	24
9	24	16	27	18	30	21	33	23	36	26	39	28
10	27	19	31	22	34	24	37	27	41	30	44	33
11			34	25	38	28	42	31	46	34	50	37
12					42	31	47	35	51	38	55	42
13							51	39	56	43	61	47
14									61	47	66	51
15											72	56

BRAIN SECTION ILLUSTRATIONS

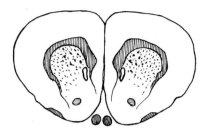

Anterior 2.5 mm

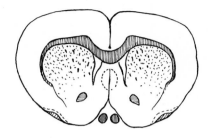

Anterior 2.0 mm

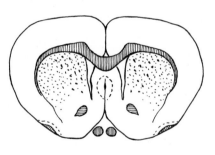

Anterior 1.5 mm

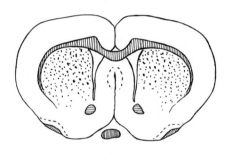

Anterior 1.0 mm

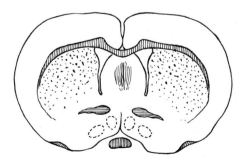

Anterior 0.5 mm

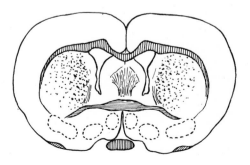

Bregma 0 mm

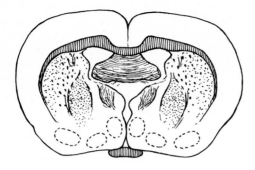

Posterior 0.5 mm

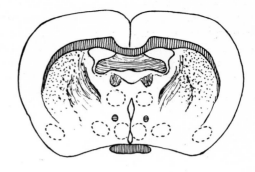

Posterior 1.0 mm

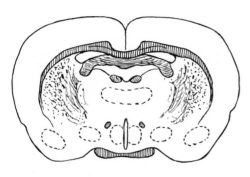

Posterior 1.5 mm

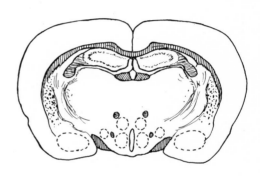

Posterior 2.0 mm

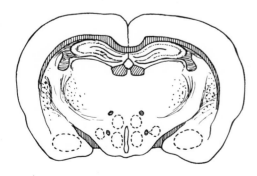

Posterior 2.5 mm

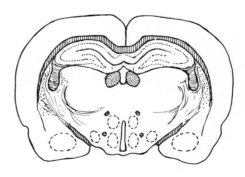

Posterior 3.0 mm

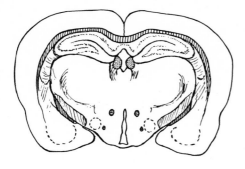

Posterior 3.5 mm

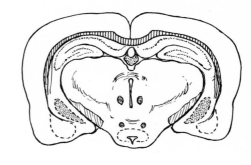

Posterior 4.0 mm

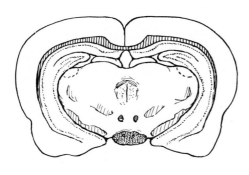

Posterior 4.5 mm

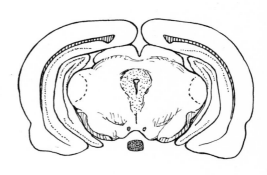

Posterior 5.0 mm

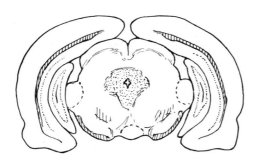

Posterior 5.5 mm

BRAIN SECTION ILLUSTRATIONS

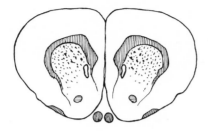

Anterior 2.5 mm

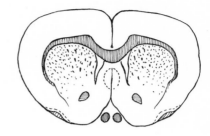

Anterior 2.0 mm

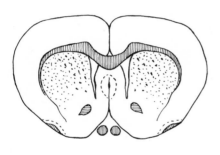

Anterior 1.5 mm

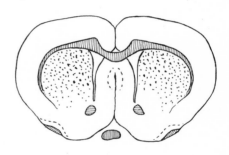

Anterior 1.0 mm

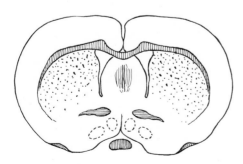

Anterior 0.5 mm

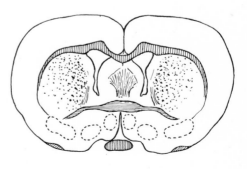

Bregma 0 mm

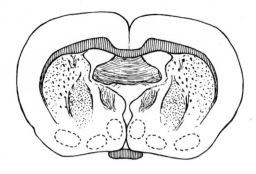

Posterior 0.5 mm

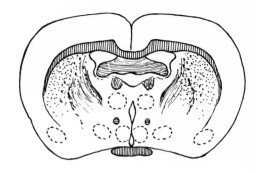

Posterior 1.0 mm

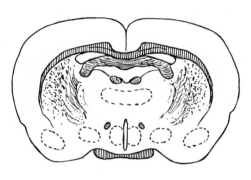

Posterior 1.5 mm

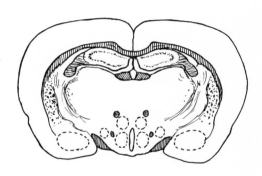

Posterior 2.0 mm

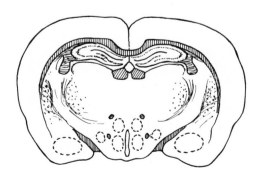

Posterior 2.5 mm

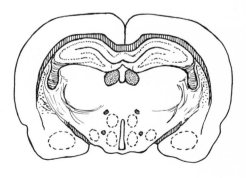

Posterior 3.0 mm

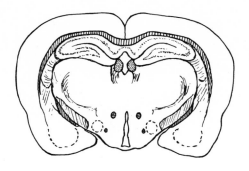

Posterior 3.5 mm

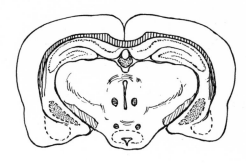

Posterior 4.0 mm

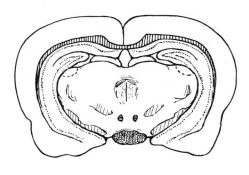

Posterior 4.5 mm

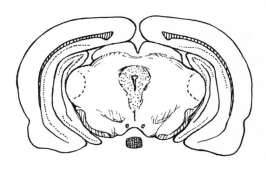

Posterior 5.0 mm

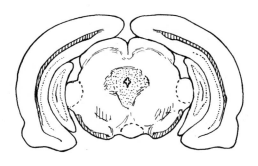

Posterior 5.5 mm

BRAIN SECTION ILLUSTRATIONS

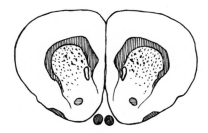

Anterior 2.5 mm

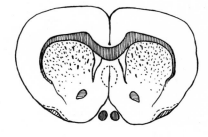

Anterior 2.0 mm

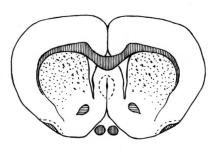

Anterior 1.5 mm

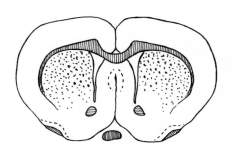

Anterior 1.0 mm

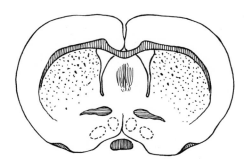

Anterior 0.5 mm

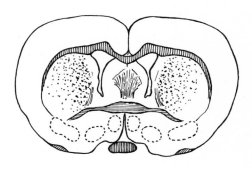

Bregma 0 mm

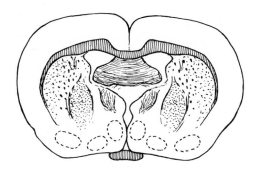

Posterior 0.5 mm

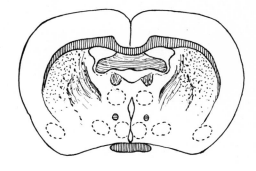

Posterior 1.0 mm

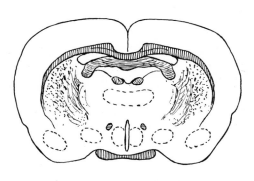

Posterior 1.5 mm

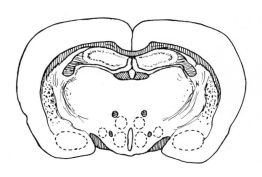

Posterior 2.0 mm

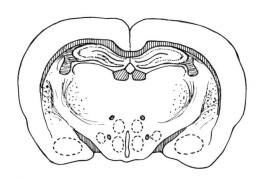

Posterior 2.5 mm

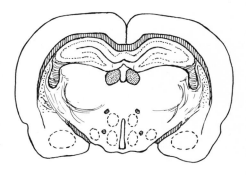

Posterior 3.0 mm

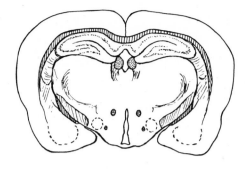

Posterior 3.5 mm

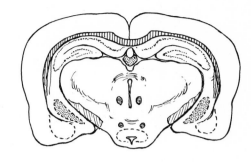

Posterior 4.0 mm

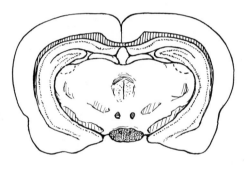

Posterior 4.5 mm

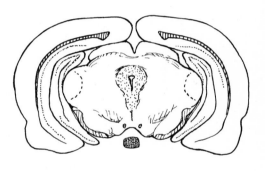

Posterior 5.0 mm

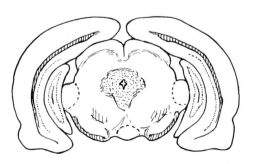

Posterior 5.5 mm

BRAIN SECTION ILLUSTRATIONS

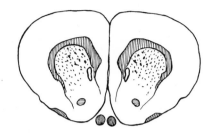

Anterior 2.5 mm

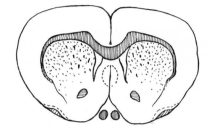

Anterior 2.0 mm

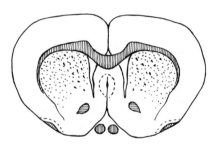

Anterior 1.5 mm

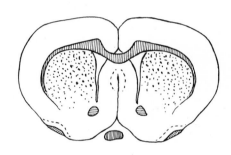

Anterior 1.0 mm

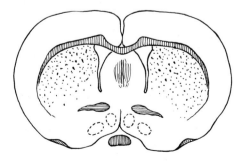

Anterior 0.5 mm

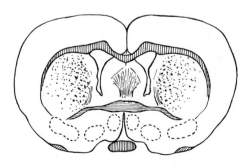

Bregma 0 mm

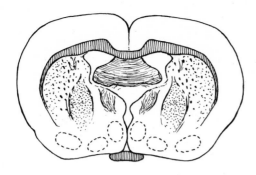

Posterior 0.5 mm

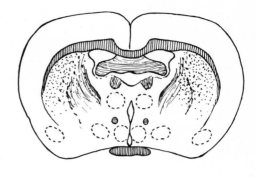

Posterior 1.0 mm

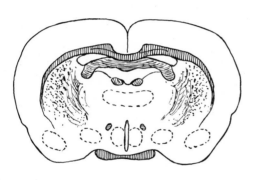

Posterior 1.5 mm

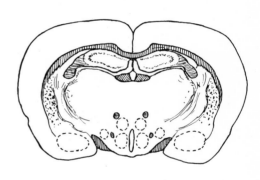

Posterior 2.0 mm

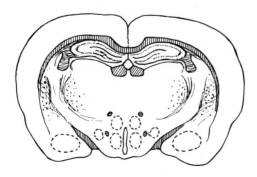

Posterior 2.5 mm

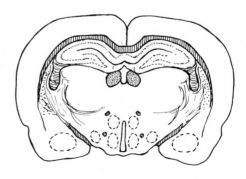

Posterior 3.0 mm

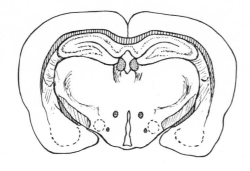

Posterior 3.5 mm

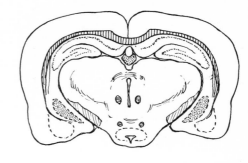

Posterior 4.0 mm

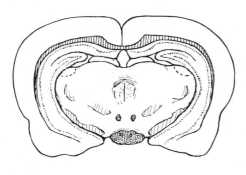

Posterior 4.5 mm

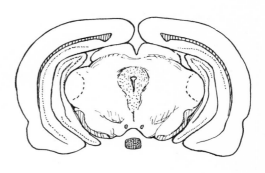

Posterior 5.0 mm

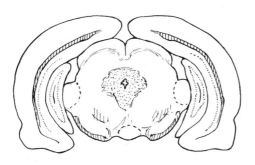

Posterior 5.5 mm

REFERENCES

Part A.

Hoebel, B. G., 1965. Hypothalamic lesions by electro-cauterization: disinhibition of feeding and self-stimulation. *Science* **149**, 452–453.

Hoebel, B. G., and P. Teitelbaum, 1962. Hypothalamic control of feeding and self-stimulation. *Science* **135**, 375–377.

Part B.

Davidson, J. M. Activation of the male rat's sexual behavior by intracerebral implantation of androgen. *Endocrinology* **79**, 783–794.

Heimer, L., and K. Larsson, 1964. Drastic changes in the mating behavior of male rats following lesions in the junction of diencephalon and mesencephalon. *Experientia* **20**, 460.

Heimer, L., and K. Larsson, 1966-67. Impairment of mating in male rats following lesions in the preoptic-anterior hypothalamic continuum. *Brain Res.* **3**, 248–267.

Lisk, R. D., 1966. Inhibitory centers in sexual behavior in the male rat. *Science* **152**, 669–670.

Lisk, R.D., 1967. Neural localization for androgen activation of copulatory behavior in the male rat. *Endocrinology* **80**, 754–761.

Lisk, R. D., 1968. Copulatory activity of male rats following placement of preoptic-anterior hypothalamic lesions. *Exp. Brain Res.* **5**, 306–313.

Part C.

Douglas, R. L., and R. C. Isaacson, 1964. Hippocampal lesions and activity. *Psychon. Sci.* **1**, 187–188.

Kim, C. 1960. Nest building, general activity and salt preference of rats following hippocampal ablation. *J. Comp. Physiol. Psychol.* **53**, 11–16.

Kimble, D. P., 1963. The effects of bilateral hippocampal lesions in rats. *J. Comp. Physiol. Psychol.* **56**, 273–283.

Leaton, R. N., 1965. Exploratory behavior in rats with hippocampal lesions. *J. Comp. Physiol. Psychol.* **59**, 325–332.

Roberts, W. W., W. N. Dember, and M. Brodwick, 1962. Alternation and exploration in rats with hippocampal lesions. *J. Comp. Physiol. Psychol.* **55**, 695–700.

Sengstake, C. B., 1968. Habituation and activity patterns of rats with large hippocampal lesions under various drive conditions. *J. Comp. Physiol. Psychol.* **65**, 504–506.

Teitelbaum, H., and P. Milner, 1963. Activity changes following partial hippocampal lesions in rats. *J. Comp. Physiol. Psychol.* **56**, 284–289.

Part D.

Olds, J., 1956. Pleasure centers in the brain. *Sci. Amer.* **195** (4), 105–106. Offprint 470.

Olds, J., 1958. Self-stimulation of the brain. *Science* **127**, 315–324.

Olds, J., 1961. Differential effects of drives and drugs on self-stimulation at different brain sites. In D. E. Sheer (Ed.), *Electrical stimulation of the brain*, pp. 351–366. Austin, University of Texas Press.

Skinner, B.F., 1951. How to Teach Animals. *Sci. Amer.* **185** (6), 26–29. Offprint 423.

Part E.

Mann, H. B., and D. R., Whitney, 1947. On a test of whether one or two random variables is stochastically larger than the other. *Ann. Math. Stat.* **18**, 50–60.

Moses, L. E., 1952. Non-parametric statistics for psychological research. *Psych. Bull.* **49**, 122–143.

Runyon, R. P., and A. Haber, 1967. *Fundamentals of behavioral statistics.* Reading, Mass., Addison-Wesley. (Good section on nonparametric statistics.)

Siegel, S., 1956. *Nonparametric statistics for the behavioral sciences.* New York, McGraw-Hill.

Wilcoxon, F., and R. A. Wilcox, 1964. *Some rapid approximate statistical procedures.* New York, American Cyanamid Co.

SOURCES OF MATERIALS

Estradiol Benzoate and Progesterone may be obtained from the Schering Corporation (1011 Morris Avenue, Union, New Jersey 07083) as "Progymon" and "Prolution" respectively. The commercial strength may be diluted with peanut oil (which can be purchased from a grocery store) so that a quantity of about .1 cc can be administered subcutaneously. See *Sources of Materials* at the end of Section 2 for a list of other materials and equipment that will be needed for the neuropsychological experiments.

THE RAT BRAIN IN SECTION:
A STEREOTAXIC ATLAS

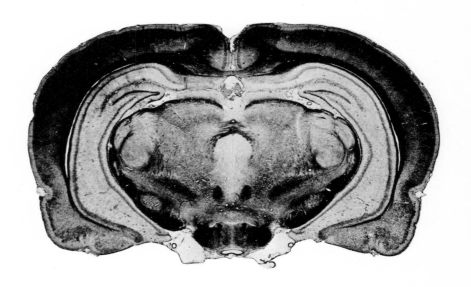

INTRODUCTION

THE PURPOSE OF THE ATLAS

This stereotaxic atlas is designed to serve two purposes. One is to aid in identification of certain structures on thin sections of the rat brain. A second purpose is to provide stereotaxic coordinates for lowering electrodes or cannulae into certain areas of the brain.

Because of the constant relation of internal brain structures to landmarks of the skull, it is possible to locate various brain structures in three dimensions with the use of skull landmarks. The landmarks employed vary in different animals. In the dog and cat, for example, they are the lower margin of the bony orbit of the eye, and the bony ear canal. For the rat many research investigators make use of the bony ear canal (the interaural line) and the bottom edge of the upper jaw just behind the first incisors. In this atlas the bregma is the main landmark. The bregma is the site at which the coronal and sagittal sutures of the skull intersect. Use of the bregma instead of the bony ear canal is desirable for two reasons: (1) many structures of the brain that are studied in experimental brain research, especially in neuropsychology, are near the transverse vertical plane of the bregma, and if this landmark is used for a zero point reference, there is less variation between rats of different size;

(2) because some individuals have difficulty in placing bars (ear bars) precisely in the bony ear canals, use of the bregma minimizes the inaccurate electrode placement that results if the bony ear canal is to be the landmark.

To use this atlas for stereotaxic surgery, the incisor bar (Figure 4-1) should be adjusted so that the point at bregma is level (with respect to the stereotaxic frame) with the point at lambda (Figure 4-2). For rats weighing about 200 g this will tilt the skull so that the incisor bar is approximately 3 mm below the level of the ear bars. Because the suture lines of most skulls are very wavy, it is a good practice to use the approximate middle of the wavy line of the sagittal suture as the midline, and also to determine the bregma by the intersection of the middle of the wavy lines of the coronal suture with the midpoint of the sagittal suture.

READING THE ATLAS

The sections shown are .5 mm apart. The transverse position of each brain section in millimeters anterior or posterior to the bregma is indicated on top of each section. The scale along the bottom of each section indicates the lateral distance, in millimeters, from the sagittal suture or midline of the brain. The vertical distance, in millimeters, from the surface of the skull (at the anteroposterior and lateral positions of the

445

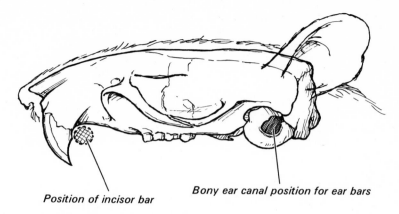

Position of incisor bar

Bony ear canal position for ear bars

FIGURE 4-1. *Relationship of the skull and overlying soft tissue (ear, eye) to the positions of the ear bars and the incisor bar.*

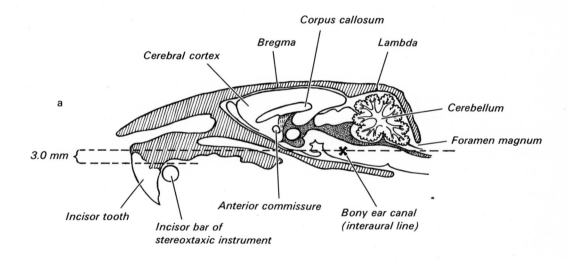

Corpus callosum

Bregma

Lambda

Cerebral cortex

a

Cerebellum

Foramen magnum

3.0 mm

Incisor tooth

Incisor bar of stereoxtaxic instrument

Anterior commissure

Bony ear canal (interaural line)

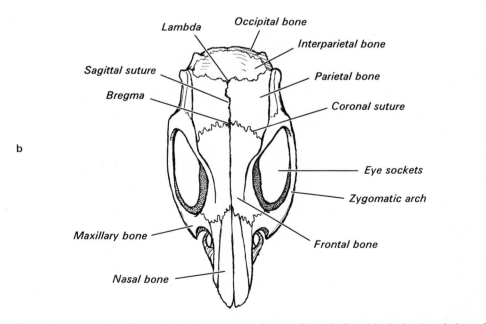

Lambda

Occipital bone

Interparietal bone

Sagittal suture

Parietal bone

Bregma

Coronal suture

b

Eye sockets

Zygomatic arch

Maxillary bone

Frontal bone

Nasal bone

FIGURE 4-2. *Relationship of the skull to the brain;* a. *midsagittal view of the skull and brain;* b. *dorsal view of the skull.*

section) is indicated along the side of each section. The scale of the coordinates of the sections in the atlas is based on measurements from rats weighing about 200 g. For rats weighing more than 300 g there should be a 10% adjustment added to each coordinate.

When a structure appears on more than one section, it may be labeled on only one of the sections in order to avoid crowding of labels. Some structures that do not stain differentially are indicated by a dotted outline that only approximates the location of the actual structure.* Each drawing is accompanied by a photomicrograph illustrating the actual appearance of stained section through the approximate area.

*For a more detailed illustration of the internal structure of the rat brain in the same approximate plane as this atlas the reader should consult the volume by J. F. R. König and R. A. Klippel, *The Rat Brain. A Stereotaxic atlas of the forebrain and lower parts of the brain stem*. Williams and Wilkins Company, Baltimore, 1963.

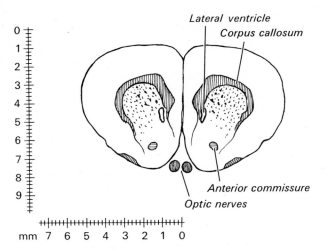

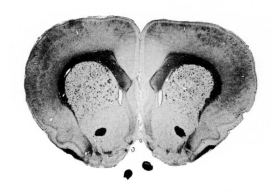

Anterior 2.5 mm

Lateral ventricle
Corpus callosum
Anterior commissure
Optic nerves

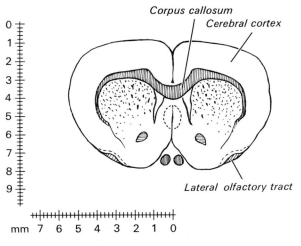

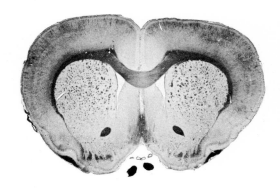

Anterior 2.0 mm

Corpus callosum
Cerebral cortex
Lateral olfactory tract

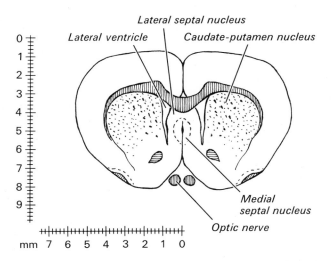

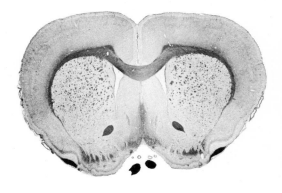

Anterior 1.5 mm

Lateral septal nucleus
Lateral ventricle
Caudate-putamen nucleus
Medial septal nucleus
Optic nerve

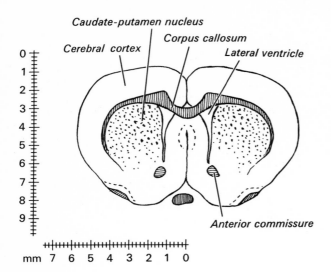

Caudate-putamen nucleus
Cerebral cortex
Corpus callosum
Lateral ventricle

Anterior commissure

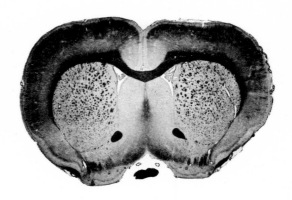

Anterior 1.0 mm

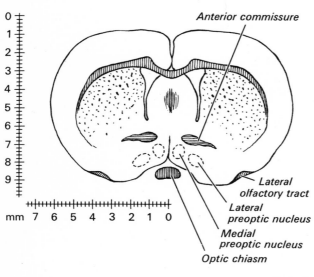

Anterior commissure

Lateral olfactory tract
Lateral preoptic nucleus
Medial preoptic nucleus
Optic chiasm

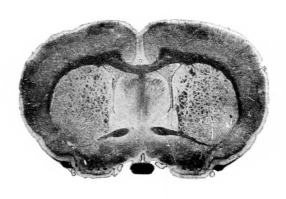

Anterior 0.5 mm

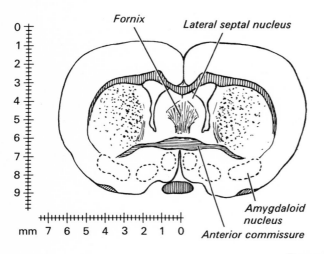

Fornix
Lateral septal nucleus

Amygdaloid nucleus
Anterior commissure

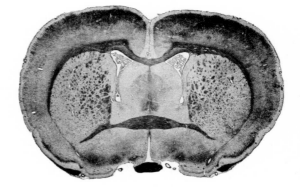

Bregma 0 mm

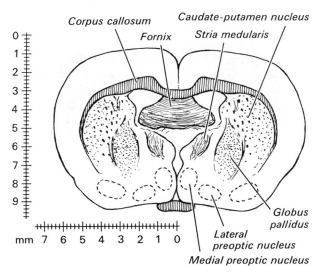

Corpus callosum
Fornix
Caudate-putamen nucleus
Stria medularis
Globus pallidus
Lateral preoptic nucleus
Medial preoptic nucleus

mm 7 6 5 4 3 2 1 0

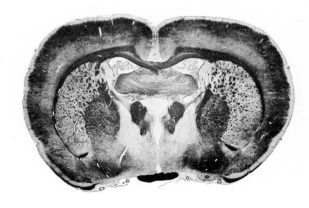

Posterior 0.5 mm

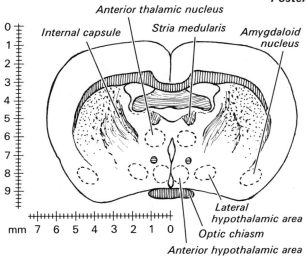

Internal capsule
Anterior thalamic nucleus
Stria medularis
Amygdaloid nucleus
Lateral hypothalamic area
Optic chiasm
Anterior hypothalamic area

mm 7 6 5 4 3 2 1 0

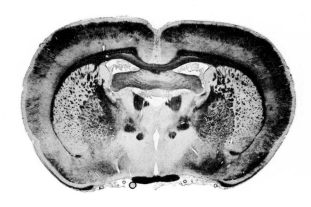

Posterior 1.0 mm

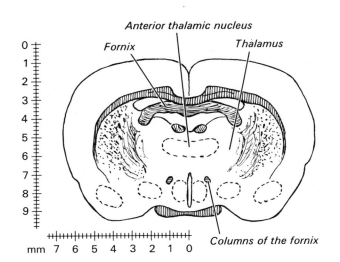

Fornix
Anterior thalamic nucleus
Thalamus
Columns of the fornix

mm 7 6 5 4 3 2 1 0

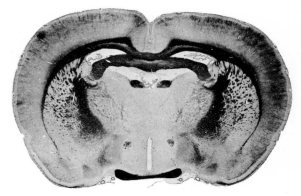

Posterior 1.5 mm

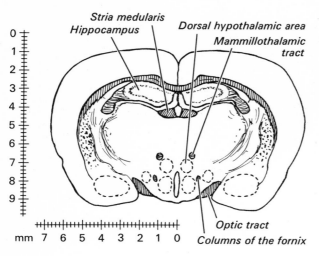

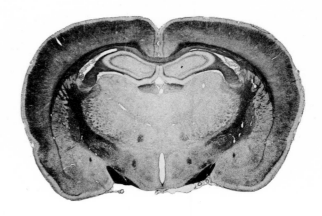

Stria medularis
Hippocampus
Dorsal hypothalamic area
Mammillothalamic tract
Optic tract
Columns of the fornix

Posterior 2.0 mm

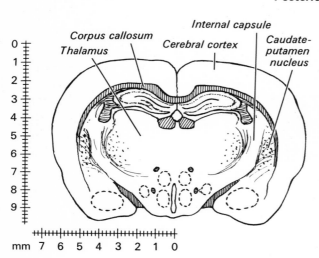

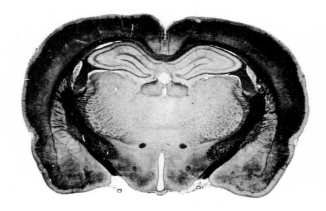

Corpus callosum
Thalamus
Internal capsule
Cerebral cortex
Caudate-putamen nucleus

Posterior 2.5 mm

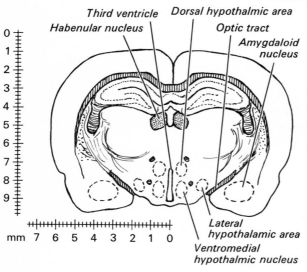

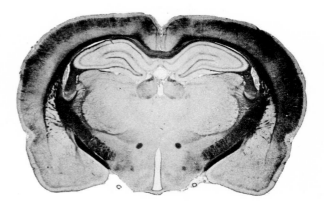

Third ventricle
Habenular nucleus
Dorsal hypothalmic area
Optic tract
Amygdaloid nucleus
Lateral hypothalamic area
Ventromedial hypothalmic nucleus

Posterior 3.0 mm

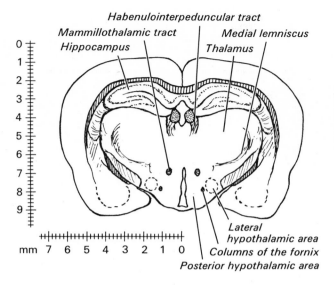

Mammillothalamic tract
Habenulointerpeduncular tract
Hippocampus
Medial lemniscus
Thalamus

Lateral hypothalamic area
Columns of the fornix
Posterior hypothalamic area

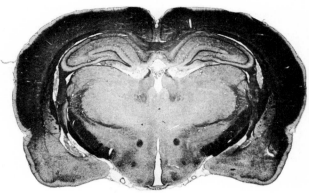

Posterior 3.5 mm

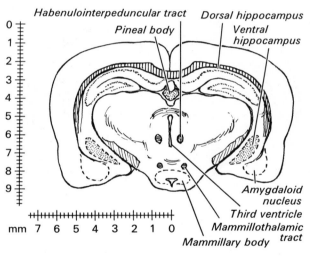

Habenulointerpeduncular tract
Pineal body
Dorsal hippocampus
Ventral hippocampus

Amygdaloid nucleus
Third ventricle
Mammillothalamic tract
Mammillary body

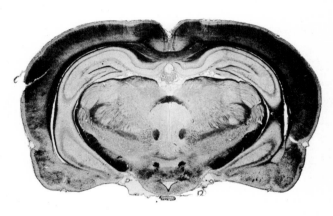

Posterior 4.0 mm

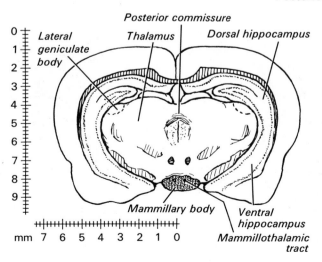

Posterior commissure
Lateral geniculate body
Thalamus
Dorsal hippocampus

Mammillary body
Ventral hippocampus
Mammillothalamic tract

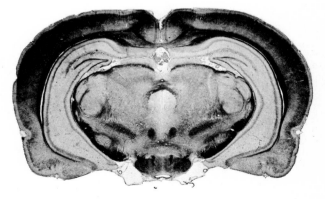

Posterior 4.5 mm

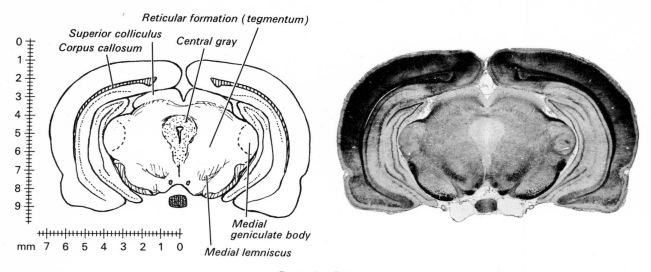

Posterior 5.0 mm

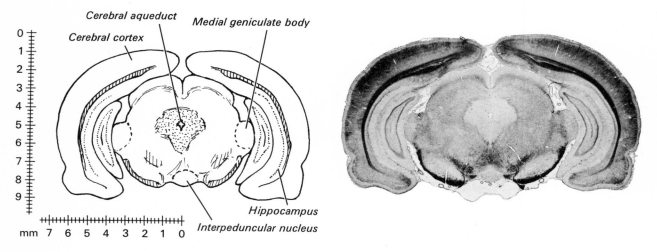

Posterior 5.5 mm